Is God a Virus?

Is God a Virus?
Genes, Culture and Religion

The Gresham Lectures, 1992–3

JOHN BOWKER

For Margaret

'There's light —
Light all about me, and I move to it.'

First published in Great Britain 1995
The Society for Promoting Christian Knowledge
Holy Trinity Church
Marylebone Road
London NW1 4DU

British Library Cataloguing-in-Publication Data
A catalogue record for this book is available
from the British Library

ISBN 0-281-04812-6

Typeset by Pioneer Associates, Perthshire
Printed in Great Britain by
Mackays of Chatham plc., Chatham, Kent

Contents

Contents

Preface

Gresham College was founded in 1597 by Sir Thomas
Gresham, an Elizabethan financier who is perhaps best
remembered for the establishment of the Royal Exchange.
A friend of Francis Bacon, he was much concerned that the
benefits of 'the new learning' should not be lost to the City
of London. His initiative was a first step towards the
founding of the Royal Society. His College has been maintained, in various forms, to the present day, always in close
connection with the City of London. Its main continuing
activity has been the appointment of seven professors 'sufficiently learned to read the lectures of divyntye, astronomy,
musicke and geometry' (appointed by the Corporation of
the City of London), and 'meete to read the lectures of
lawe, phissicke and rhetoricke' (appointed by the Worship-
ful Company of Mercers). An eighth chair of Commerce, the
Mercer's School Memorial Chair, was added in 1985. Since
the sixteenth century, the Gresham Professors have given
free public lectures in the City.

A major concern of the lectures is to share with a wider
public the results and directions of current research in the
various disciplines, and to point towards their application
to contemporary issues. This book contains lectures which
were given in 1992 and 1993 on issues arising from the
explosion of recent (and often very controversial) work in
the field of genetic and cultural evolution.

ix

Part I describes the work which has led up to the claim, made by Richard Dawkins, that God is a virus. This work is related (though often critically) to the proposals about gene-culture coevolution, which are known as Sociobiology. This part of the book looks at these proposals, and suggests that the perspective of 'the selfish gene' rests on very mistaken assumptions about how much the genes can actually do in isolation.

Nevertheless, an evolutionary perspective throws important light on the nature of religions and, in particular, on the question of why religions are involved in almost all the most intransigent and violent conflicts in the world. After an exploration of what religions are, and of why they are so dangerous, Part II ends with some suggestions concerning the relationship of religions to each other.

Part III turns to a much more specific issue — the light thrown on the status of women in religions when this is put in a context of gene-culture considerations. This is given focus by looking at arguments which were advanced against the ordination of women in the debate in the Church of England. Specific appeal was made both to the 'natural nature' of women and to culture. These arguments are evaluated in the context of gene-culture coevolution, not simply as a commentary on a past debate, but much more because the debate continues (not least among Roman Catholics), and because, even when a decision has been made to ordain women, the issue of reception (that is, of the attitudes that people have towards women in the ordained ministry) is still very much alive. It remains important, therefore, to examine the foundation of these attitudes in the use that is made of genetic and cultural arguments about the nature of women and their role in the Church.

The book, therefore, moves from the general to a particular case study, testing current theories in gene-culture coevolution (and questioning whether that phrase is, in fact, a wise one), and showing how the results illuminate our understanding of religions.

Acknowledgements

I am deeply grateful to the electors to the professorship, to Peter Nailor, the Provost, and Maggie Butcher, the Academic Administrator. At a time when illness compelled me into early retirement, Gresham College kept me in touch with academic conversation and colleagues. In particular, Professor Francis Cox read through Part I of this book, and his suggestions have been gratefully incorporated. For the patience and support of the College, my thanks.

My thanks also to Quinton Deeley. His contribution to Part I of this book has been of such a kind that he is, in effect, the joint author of it. After we had met at Cambridge, where I supervised his dissertation on biogenetic structuralism, he made the remarkable decision that, if he was to understand the issues adequately, he should start again and train as a medical student. Several years on, he is close to qualifying. In the meantime, the roles have been reversed, and he has kept me informed of developments in the field, changing my own way of looking at developmental issues and at the careless language often used when discussing them. When I was too ill to deliver the Gresham Lectures, he took the script and delivered them instead. My gratitude to him is equalled only by my admiration at his determination to pursue the truth.

And finally, a particular 'thank you' to Margaret, my wife, who brought me through some difficult years of illness and alone made these lectures and this book possible.

PART I
Is God a Virus?

*The publishers acknowledge with gratitude
the help and support of Gresham College
in the publication of this book.*

Introduction

I am: yet what I am none cares or knows,
My friends forsake me like a memory lost . . . .

So begins John Clare's deeply moving poem 'Written in
Northampton County Asylum'. Ironically, John Clare has
more 'friends' — or at least admirers — now than when he
was alive, even after the spectacular success of his *Poems
Descriptive of Rural Life and Scenery* in 1820; and, certainly, we would claim to 'know' more about his bereft
uncertainty — the 'what I am' — than was possible in the
first half of the nineteenth century. Of his mental disorder
(which he shared with, among many others, Cowper,
Christopher Smart, Goethe, Newton, and Samuel Johnson)
we would say that it was a form of cyclothymia, combined
with delusions, and we would not leave these phrases
entirely empty of content.

Clare's delusions took the form of thinking that he was
the poet Byron, that he was a boxer or a wrestler of the
time, that he had married his childhood sweetheart, and
that his real wife was, in fact, his second wife. Already an
answer to the question, 'Who or what am I?', becomes complicated. We are more inclined, therefore, to answer such
questions, not by searching for an atman (soul) or essence
of a person (as earlier philosophies or religions might have
done), nor by the search for a self or soul in the midst of
such confusion. We tend to look instead for the sources or
causes of behaviour and character, for the *reasons* for people

3

exhibiting the behaviour or character that they do. Thus, we look at the statistical distribution of cyclothymic mood disorders, and find them occurring with unusual frequency in groups of close relatives: as these match the statistical predictions of genetic models, we therefore infer that there is a genetic contribution to this condition (see, for example, Gershon, E. S., *et al.*, 'Transmitted Factors in the Morbid Risk of Affective Disorders: A Controlled Study', *Journal of Psychiatric Research*, XII, 1975, pp. 283–99).

Our genetic inheritance clearly contributes greatly to the 'what I am' of human — or, for that matter, of other living — nature. Why is it the case, for example, that you are not three hundred feet high with a weight of a hundred tons? These are, at present, the largest living things, redwood trees and whales. The smallest mycoplasmas, in contrast, are truly minute, able to contain only about a thousand protein molecules. Then, we may ask, why are there no hundred-ton insects, nor any microscopic birds? 'Why do all multicellular animals, from tiny nematode worms to whales, have cells about the same size?' asks R. M. Alexander when reviewing T. A. McMahon and J. T. Bonner, *On Size and Life* (in *Times Higher Educ. Supp.*, 6.4.84, p. 25). It is only the start of an answer to say that genetic processes contribute to the size and form of living appearances — but, it *is* the start of an answer.

How might the answer continue? Certainly with reference to the environment, which sets its own limits on successful or possible life. This means that our genetic inheritance is not the only source or cause of 'what I am'. John Clare also had a history, a biography of individual and idiosyncratic experience. He lived at a time of immense changes in agriculture, and he became the acute and exact observer of a disappearing world. He lived, that is, in a particular culture, society, place, and family — all of which formed his way of seeing, both in general and in highly specific detail. Thus, we can hardly imagine that this personal adventure had no effect on him, when, at the age of five, he wandered off alone across Emmonsales Heath:

I had imagined that the world's end was at the edge of the horizon and that a day's journey was able to find it . . . so I went on, expecting when I got to the brink of the world that I could see into its secrets the same as I could . . . see heaven by looking into the water. So I eagerly wandered on and rambled along the furze till I got out of my knowledge when the very wild flowers and birds seemed to forget me and I imagined they were the inhabitants of new countries. The very sun seemd to be a new one and shining in a different quarter of the sky. Still I felt no fear: my wonder seeking happiness had no room for it . . . Night crept on before I had time to fancy the morning was bye . . . . When I got home I found my parents in great distress and half the village about hunting me.

Quoted from ed. A. Tibble, *John Clare: The Journals,*
Essays, and the Journey from Essex
(Manchester, Carcanet New Press, 1980) pp. 9ff.

If, then, we are to give some account in our day of the 'what I am' of human nature — or if, to put it more jargonistically, we are to form a post-modernist anthropology which does justice to the evidence of current research — it would seem obvious that we have to identify two great sources or reservoirs which flow into the construction of human life and character: genes and culture. But what, so to speak, is flowing? Obviously, energy. Humans are transactions and transformations of energy in highly organized forms, subject to the laws of thermodynamics and certainly, therefore, of entropy. But so is everything else. So what, more specifically, controls the human architecture of energy into its characteristic forms — into being humans and not whales or redwood trees? The pervasive answer to this at the present time is 'information'. From genes and culture, the human body and brain are 'informed'; they are 'programmed' so that they behave in characteristic ways. There may, indeed, be individual idiosyncrasy, but it is contained within boundaries of constraint which are set by genes and culture.

Then, the question becomes one of how these two information systems interact with each other. Do the genes construct the cake on which culture simply deposits icing? Or do the genes supply the ingredients which are then made into very different kinds of cake by the recipes of different cultures? Much of the current debate is focused on exactly this issue: how *do* genes and culture, as the two sources of human nature, interact with each other? Does one dominate over the other? If so, which? Do the genes hold culture on a leash or does culture, so to speak, 'spring back' on the leash and override the elementary contribution of the genes?

It is part of the argument of this book that this is entirely the wrong way to set up the issue. But this does not alter the fact that it is the massively predominant way in which the insights of genetics have been brought to bear on old issues: in accounting for human behaviours, what weighting do we give to the innate versus the learned, the instinctive versus the acquired, nature versus nurture?

The current debates about genes and culture rest, as we shall see, on a deeply mistaken metaphor. If we can emancipate ourselves from this error, we may have a better chance of understanding the true relationship between genes and culture, and then also of applying this to other questions — in the case of this book, to the arguments from nature which have been apparent in the debate about the ordination of women, and to the nature of religion, which lends itself to so many violent and dangerous conflicts in the world.

But, how to get to that promised land? And how does this relate to Dawkins' question, 'Is God a virus?' Because to some this may be unfamiliar territory, it may be helpful to give a brief map of the ground to be covered in Part I.

First, we will look at the way in which the new understanding of genetics invaded the existing 'nature versus nurture' debate affecting greatly the understanding of human nature and behaviour. In some sense, it is obvious that both genes *and* culture contribute something to the characteristic nature of human life. For much of this century, it has been held, especially by anthropologists, that nurture and culture do all the real work. It was this dominant position which was challenged especially through the work of E. O. Wilson. He called his approach 'Socio-biology', and it included aggressive claims about the priority of genes in accounting for human nature and behaviour. Genes and culture cooperate (literally, from the Latin, 'work together'), but in such a way that culture simply acts as a protective defence for the genes. It is, therefore, a theory of gene-culture coevolution, but it gives such primacy to the genes that I intend to call it 'Strong Theory Mark I'. The account of this will introduce the terms 'the immortal' and 'the selfish' gene.

Second, we will see how culture insisted on a greater degree of independence than seemed possible in Strong Theory Mark I, and how this led to a revised statement of Sociobiology, leading to Strong Theory Mark II. The argument at this stage is that it is possible to isolate discrete cultural 'items', which have a life-history of their own. This history can be followed as these cultural items (such things as seat belts, traffic regulations and Gresham College) 'track' and, ultimately, defend the necessary conditions for the replication of genetic information — conditions that are set by natural selection in straightforward, neo-Darwinian evolutionary terms. These cultural items are called 'cultur-gens' by Wilson, but 'memes' by Dawkins.

So third, we will see how the relative independence of cultural items (the fact that, to some extent — to what extent exactly is disputed — they follow histories of their own) has led to Weak Theories of gene-culture coevolution. Weak Theories allow that culturgens or memes may, in fact, be in the process of being tested for fitness, by the contribution they make to enhancing the probability of gene-replication or in changing gene-frequencies. However, they also develop an independent history of their own, which has to be evaluated for its continuing worth to human communities on other grounds as well. Cultural items, therefore, may be selected on grounds of cultural fitness.

Dawkins, who puts forward a Weak Theory, then presses further: genes and memes may indeed interact by way of mutual enhancement, but memes are so sufficiently distinct that they have to be regarded as a *second* evolving and self-replicating system of evolution. His major question is the extent to which the well-established conditions of gene-replication provide an *analogy* for meme-replication, so that (to put it over-simply) memes mimic the ways in which genes perpetuate themselves from one generation to the next. Taking 'A' to stand for 'analogy', I have called this 'Weak Theory A'. It is Weak Theory A which produces the claim that God is a virus.

All this, so far, will be a brief survey of how we have reached the present position in the debate about gene-culture coevolution, and of how we have reached the claim that God is a virus. But it remains in the context of that question, 'I am; yet *what* I am, none cares or knows'. Interestingly in this regard, Wilson called his first popular account of Sociobiology, *On Human Nature* (Harvard Univ. Press, 1978). So, although we may seem at moments to be getting lost in a thicket of jargon and complexity, the aim is to show how the current debate about gene-culture coevolution is profoundly misleading in its endeavour to deliver a more illuminating account of human nature, because it is trapped in the wrong frame of argument and explanation. In other words, we will be spending time initially reviewing arguments and propositions which are, in my view, profoundly wrong. They rest on important truths, though, and we cannot disentangle these truths — still less understand the claim that God is a virus — unless we cover this ground.

Thus, our next, fourth, stage will be to look at the difference it makes if we understand genes and culture, not as the only coercive causes of human nature, but as contributing in varying ways (very often causatively), to the formation of human life, character, and behaviour, not least by setting limits on possibility. But they are contributing to a *developmental process* in each human case, and the consequence of their contributions, therefore, cannot be the same in every case, nor can they be isolated. Thus, already, more than four thousand disorders in the human body have been identified that can be traced back to defective genes. It is not in dispute that the defective gene 'causes' the disorder, and that the disorder in question — say, cystic fibrosis — follows a predictable pathway in its effects in the human body. But it still does not produce the same consequence in the life-history of each individual concerned. By isolating the genetic cause, for the purposes of diagnosis and of research into gene-therapy, we run the risk of supposing that nothing else is relevantly or saliently causative in the formation of human nature and history. We come to the conclusion that we are gene-survival machines, and all else drops away into irrelevance.

So, the journey before us is a long one. Let us begin, therefore, at 2.06 p.m., on 21 March 1986, with a story from *The New York Times*. According to the report, it was at that time, on that day, that a strange 'sea creature' was spotted in the Central Queens swimming pool in New York by children in the Pollywog and Guppy swimming classes, '. . . who were scared half out of their wits'. The 'creature' was identified as Mr Ashita Furman. According to Yvonne Dye, the aquatic coordinator at the pool, '. . . he wore a swimming suit, goggles and snorkel, and was acting in a peculiar manner, bouncing up and down in the deep end on a pogo stick'.

According to Mr Furman, '"You don't have to be a genius to see the potential here . . . : I ask you," he said, "Is this any dumber than hanging upside down in gravity boots?" And he went on to ask the same of other fads, including mechanical bronco riding, hot-coal-walking, power-breakfasting, Argentine tango dancing, yo-yoing, playing Frisbee, Hula-hooping and collecting Garbage Pail Kids Cards.'

The reporter then asked, '"But what about the pitfalls?" "Drowning, I suppose, would be one," Mr Furman said, "and your skin can shrivel up a bit." . . . However, he is not a man who is easily discouraged or humiliated. He holds the world record for forward somersaulting — ten miles. "If you think aqua pogo is weird," he said, "you ought to see people staring at me when I'm practising somersaulting"' — which he does on a running track in the middle of the night in order to minimize humiliation: '"People come by and I get scared," he said, "but not nearly as scared as they get of me."'

The report in *The New York Times* concluded:

> The children at the pool were asked if they would like to try aqua pogo. 'No way,' said Crystal Elliott, 7 years old. 'Too weird.' 'I'll tell you something, kids,' said Felix Oleaga, a swimming instructor, as he jumped into the pool with the pogo stick. 'As you go through life, you've got to try all these new things.' 'Oh nooooooo,' said Crystal, sounding as though she saw a long, hard life ahead'.
>
> W. E. Geist, *The New York Times*, 22 March 1986, p. 11

We will return to the pool, the children, and the aqua pogo at various intervals. In the meantime, we must move on elsewhere, to a lecture room in 1978, as a lecturer stands up to speak.

1

Genes and Culture:
Nature and Nurture

In 1978, a lecturer stood up to address an academic meeting and was greeted with cries of 'Nazi, Nazi'. One demonstrator ran up, took the jug of water standing on a table near the lecturer, and poured it all over him. The lecturer was E. O. Wilson; and his reception marked a new stage in the long-running debate about the priority of nature versus nurture in the formation of human behaviours and character. The debate, put in its updated terms, is this. Human lives, it is claimed, are 'informed' by two major sources: the genes, which build our bodies and brains, and culture, which 'builds' our mental outlook and supplies the opportunities that enable us to exercise our competence. Thus, the genes build bodies which have the competence to mate successfully, thereby replicating genetic information into another generation. Culture offers (often by way of setting limits) the approved ways in which sexuality can be expressed. Humans are, therefore, 'built' by two information systems: the genetic and the cultural.

But which, if either, exercises control? If, at one extreme, the genes build bodies as survival machines, which then serve as vehicles for continuing genetic information into another generation, then one might make the case that culture is built by the genes via human brains in order to enhance the probability of gene-replication. To put it more accurately (as genes do not do anything consciously or

11

deliberately), cultural creations flourish and survive in so far as they happen to enhance the probability of gene-replication. One could then say that the genes build the body, bounded by the skin, as the first defensive boundary for themselves; culture is the second defensive 'skin' in which the genes sit. At this extreme, genes determine culture and the human behaviours associated with it, and this extreme can be called 'genetic determinism'.

However, if, at the other extreme, one regards the genes as the enabling mechanisms of culture — in the sense that genes build bodies, in the human case, that live lives and, in so doing, detach themselves from strict genetic considerations of survival and replication of genetic information — then culture is no doubt grateful to the genes, but waves them goodbye as it goes off to live a life of its own. From this perspective, then, far from culture enhancing the survival of the body until the genetic information has been replicated, culture may actually encourage people to do things that oppose such a consideration; it encourages some people to be celibate or to die for their country (often at an early age), and, in many societies, it encourages the use of birth control. If culture takes charge of the gene-built organisms and dictates which human behaviours are regarded as worthwhile, this can be called 'cultural determinism'.

Does it matter which of the two is correct — if either of them is? Yes, it matters greatly, because the answer endorsed in any culture or society will directly affect policy on virtually every major topic — from education to the treatment of criminals (indeed, in the case of these two issues, it will determine whether any difference is perceived to exist between them).

Although this book will argue that this debate is spurious, nevertheless the process has thrown up truths regarding genes and culture that will help us to understand why, for example, religions are likely to destroy human life as we know it on this planet. On a less dramatic plane, it will help us to understand why we may have a panic fear of snakes and spiders, but not of power sockets or cars. The way we understand the issues here will affect our relationships to each other — individually, socially, and politically. It will inform not only the content of our social, economic, and educational decisions, but also the style in which we make them. To take only one example: if you believe that there is a genetic base, which is cross-cultural, to all human behaviours, then you are more likely to conclude that human rights have a well-grounded foundation in human nature, and that human values have a factual basis that can be discerned dimly through the vagaries of cultural opinion — dimly, maybe, but discerned nevertheless. Benjamin Franklin saw this point with a keen and practical eye:

> God grant that not only the love of liberty but a thorough knowledge of the rights of man may pervade all the nations of the earth, so that a philosopher may set his feet anywhere on its surface and say, 'This is my country'.
> Quoted in N. Cousins, *In God We Trust*, p. 41.

If, on the other hand, you consider that the genes contribute little more than the bodies through which behaviours are expressed, and that culture is the all-important human invention, then you are more likely to conclude that rights and values are themselves social constructions, with no independent or objective foundation — they may have the virtues of utility or expediency, but they will depend for their existence and their validity on our social approval and endorsement.

There is, of course, an irony to such a conclusion. E. O. Wilson, the 'founding father' of the discipline known as Sociobiology, has argued for the *former* of those alternatives (that there is a cross-cultural genetic basis for many human behaviours), yet he has been attacked because of his attempt to demonstrate the way in which the genes hold the whole of human culture on a leash: it is the genes which determine successful or unsuccessful cultural experiments. To some, this has seemed to imply a commitment, not to human rights, but to 'social engineering', based on genetic theory, of a kind that has led to him being accused of being a neo-Nazi. That is why passions have been running so high. In 1975, a group known as the Sociobiology Study Group of Science for the People wrote a vehement letter to *The New York Review of Books*, resisting even the presentation of the arguments of Sociobiology on the grounds that such an attempt to establish the biological basis of human behaviour was a reversion to Social Darwinism, with all the ruthless consequences of both totalitarian and capitalist ideologies. Such attempts:

> . . . consistently tend to provide a genetic justification of the *status quo* and of existing privileges for certain groups according to class, race, or sex. Historically, powerful countries or ruling groups within them have drawn support for the maintenance or extension of their power from these products of the scientific community. For example, John D. Rockefeller, Sr. said, 'The growth of a large business is merely a survival of the fittest . . . . It is merely the working out of a law of nature and a law of God.' These theories provided an important basis for the enactment of sterilization laws and restrictive immigration laws by the United States between 1910 and 1930 and also for the eugenics policies which led to the establishment of gas chambers in Nazi Germany.
>
> C. J. Lumsden and E. O. Wilson, *Promethean Fire: Reflections on the origin of mind* (Cambridge, Harvard University Press, 1983), p. 39.

The accusation, as we shall see, was false, but the passion was undoubtedly real. After all, we now know how to manipulate genes, and so, for some people, eugenics pops up once more like the fright doll of a Chinese folk theatre. What is to stop us creating the kinds of people we want? Even without gene-manipulation, we can affect the distribution of gender, and, in many cultures, there is a strong preference for boys. In December, 1991, in the UK, the first centre to offer couples the chance to choose the gender of their would-be child (by attempting to separate female X-sperm from male Y-sperm and by inseminating women with sperm of the chosen type) opened.

The issue, then, as it has been understood in terms of

the traditional debate, is how to understand the ways in which genes and culture interact in producing the individuals who, in turn, produce societies and culture. It is a key question of anthropology: what makes a person the kind of entity that she or he is? Is it, essentially, the genes, which build the survival machines which, in the case of humans, extend the defensive skin of the body to the second skin of culture? At an extreme, as we have seen, this would amount to genetic determinism. Alternatively, is it culture, which is a consequence of the wide competence of the brain to pursue cooperative goals, not least through the development of language? If culture controls permissible behaviours, then, at this other extreme, as we have also seen, this would amount to cultural determinism.

Even if one stops short of *determinism*, it is still clearly the case that advocates of culture dominating the genetic endowment have held sway through most of this century. The reason is not surprising. When the work of Mendel was rediscovered, which demonstrated the effect of 'elements' — known now as genes — in dictating the character of peas through successive generations, it seemed to some that the way lay open to an even more scientific approach to eugenics than had already been achieved by breeders of cattle for agricultural shows. The racial theories of the Nazis were an extreme step down an inviting road. Standing across that road was the immensely able and respected anthropologist Franz Boas. Well aware of the consequences involved, he recruited research students, including Ruth Benedict and Margaret Mead, to argue the exact opposite (and to find the evidence for the opposite), the view that while there is indeed a common human ability to make judgements, which is the basis of choice, nevertheless cultures are a consequence of these choices — they are not variations on a genetic theme. In a review, in 1926, of Malinowski's *Crime and Custom*, he commented:

> There remains a fundamental difference between a complex phenomenon that has grown up historically, and generalised scientific laws. The complexity of historical events is such

that the cultural life of any people and of any tribe can be understood only as an outgrowth of those unique conditions under which it has lived.

On this view, therefore, everything that matters in the human case is acquired in cultural transmission and education. Furthermore, cultures can be rapidly changed through re-education, in a way that is plainly impossible with eugenics. This explains the reforming zeal of, in particular, Margaret Mead: from Samoa and New Guinea (*Coming of Age in Samoa*, 1928 and *Growing Up in New Guinea*, 1930), the lessons might be learned that would lead to a re-formation of the sexual mores of American youth.

Here one can see the seeds of the passion with which anthropologists have been inclined to resist the invasion of biology into the explanation of human behaviour (so much so that Freeman's analysis of Margaret Mead's research data, in *Margaret Mead and Samoa: The making and unmaking of an anthropological myth*, suggested that she had organized the data to tell the 'Boas' story'). The equally influential Alfred Kroeber declared that between anthropology and biology there is fixed 'an eternal chasm'.

This 'chasm' is often summarized as 'nature versus nurture' — and it leads to the contrast between naturalism and cultural relativism. 'Naturalism' is the claim that there is enough fixed in human nature — that is, invariant across cultures and types of social organization — to form a premise in proposals about political and social order. 'Cultural relativists' hold the view that the fixed elements (such as breathing, eating, and reproducing) are rudimentary, and that there are many equally valid cultural variations on these elementary human themes. Human societies are, as it were, different stories told about the near-infinite human possibilities, so that their highly divergent cultural constructions can thus be regarded as different texts to be interpreted — with some cross-reference to other texts, but primarily on their own terms. To understand them is a work of exegesis or of hermeneutics, in which the fact of diversity is paramount. Novels may indeed be novels, and portraits portraits, but no literary or art critics believe that their task is confined to the demonstration of some universal in which the diversities of style, method, and content are negligible.

However, the vast and rapid expansion of our understanding of what genes are and of what they do has led others, more recently, to suggest that Kroeber's chasm *can* be bridged, and, indeed, that it *must* be bridged if we are to secure a wiser appreciation of how genes and culture *together* constitute human nature and action; and thus we arrive at the dominating interactionist framework of discussion.

So, the question — within this interactionist framework — necessarily becomes, 'Where does the emphasis in building this bridge mainly rest? On the genetic or on the cultural side? If it rests on both, how do we measure the relative contribution of each? If we think of a spectrum, ranging from genetic determinism at one end to cultural determinism at the other, we can see immediately that no one who has given the matter any thought is an unqualified determinist at either end; between the two extremes lie a range of theories. At the genetic end of the spectrum are those which argue that genes are the controlling units of selection, and that culture serves the genes in their quest for survival: genes, therefore hold culture on a leash. These we can call 'strong theories' of gene-culture coevolution. At the cultural end are those which see culture as a separate information system flowing into the construction of human life and character, which follows its own evolutionary history. It is hooked on to gene-evolution in various ways, but it is not tied to the genes. It has extended, or even slipped off, the leash of the genes. These we can call 'weak theories' of coevolution.

2

Genes, Genotypes, and Phenotypes

In the move towards both strong and weak theories, socio-biology has been a pioneering enterprise. But, in order to understand what is at issue between them, and how they yield the argument that God is a virus, we need first to understand how they have been developed as theories.

Sociobiology is founded on the developed fusion of Darwin and Mendel, which is known as neo-Darwinian orthodoxy. Darwin was exercised by the immense diversity and variety of species which nevertheless exhibited, in groups among themselves, very close approximations of morphology (in outward appearance). The work on fossils of extinct animals had already suggested that there was a correspondence between extinct and living animals, which argued in favour of uniform processes continuing through time (hence uniformitarianism, as opposed to catastrophism, which argued that major changes in the geological structure of the Earth were caused by violent upheavals, interspersed with periods of stability). Darwin's voyage on the Beagle (1831–6) took him to the Galapagos Islands, where the geographical isolation of each island made it clear that each variant of a species (the key example was the variation between the Galapagos' finches) could develop from a common ancestor, but could develop adaptively in different ways. In *The Origin of Species* (1859), he argued that organisms produce more reproductive units than give rise to mature individuals, yet the numbers of individuals in species remain fairly constant. Consequently, there must be a high rate of mortality. In the competition for survival, individuals in a species are not all identical, but exhibit variations in all characteristics. It follows that some variants will succeed more than others, and that the parents of the next generation will be selected from those whose variations have helped them most to adapt to the conditions of their environment. As it is an observable fact that offspring resemble parents, it can be assumed that subsequent generations will maintain and improve on the adaptations achieved by their parents, thus taking part in a process of gradual change.

That last argument was something of an assumption, because Darwin did not know how acquired, advantageous characteristics could be secured and transmitted to subsequent generations. In other words, he knew nothing of genetics, even though Mendel was doing his work on successive generations of peas at much the same time. However, it was not until 1900 that Mendel's published work was rediscovered, and his basic insight established, that there must be units (Mendel called them 'elements') of inheritance that control the strict sequences of recurrence in successive generations. These units of inheritance are what we now call 'genes' — chain-like molecules of nucleic acids (usually DNA, but RNA in some viruses), which are normally located on the chromosomes, and are found mainly in the nucleus of the cell. The cell is the basic unit of living matter from which all plants and animals are made. In the words of Ernest Borek:

> Water, proteins, nucleic acids, fats, sugars and salts, such are the mundane substances the chemist finds within the living cell. Certainly these are not 'such stuff as dreams are made on'. And yet, on such stuff is built the edifice of the improbable dream that is life. All the greater, therefore, is the miracle of life.
>
> *The Atoms Within Us* (New York, Columbia University Press, 1980).

Genes, therefore, are a part of the developmental process of the cell, which is the basis of life. The DNA molecule contains phosphate, deoxyribose (a sugar), and four substances (adenine, guanine, cytosine, and thymine — AGCT), which are known as 'bases'. In mammalian cells, the DNA molecule is a helix, formed by two complementary strands of bases running parallel to each other, but in opposite directions. The strands are held together by bonds between bases, with A always pairing with T, and C with G. Outside the strands are linkages, or 'backbones', which are made up of phosphate and deoxyribose, so that the molecule is made up of a sequence of nucleotides, with base linked to a sugar linked to a phosphate. The order of bases in DNA specifies the sequence of amino acids in proteins, in groups of three bases: thus GTG specifies histidine. A particular gene (i.e., a particular section of DNA) leads to a corresponding structure of a specific protein or part of a protein. The stability of this ordering constitutes the genetic code.

DNA replicates itself every time a cell divides (thereby conserving its sequence). It does this by 'unzipping' itself, so that the famous 'double helix' of its construction unwinds into two strands. Each of these then acts as a template on which another strand forms, so that the two original strands of the double helix become four. Replication of DNA occurs when the two strands unwind and separate so that each then pairs with free complementary nucleotides. DNA leads to the production of proteins when its sequence is copied on to RNA in the same way, except that in RNA thymine is replaced by uracil (U). The RNA (messenger or mRNA) leaves the nucleus of the cell and reaches structures in the cell known as ribosomes where, with the help of transfer RNA, the assembly of the amino acids takes place. The sequences of three consecutive bases in mRNA which code for amino acids are known as codons.

In this process, DNA never leaves the nucleus or other centres of nucleic acid concentration in the cell. It is effectively inert and, as Calow put it,

> . . . the message passing along the communication channels established by these self-replicating systems (from one

template to another) was, and still is, basically very dull
and very simple — being just 'transmit me'.

P. Calow, *Biological Machines: A Cybernetic Approach to Life* (London, Arnold, 1976) p. 120.

Despite the caution of those words, the orthodox view of
contemporary biology speaks in far more extravagant language — in terms, that is, of codes, information and
instruction. While there is indeed a legitimate sense in which
one can speak of the genetic code, it is, as we shall see, an
illegitimate misuse of metaphor to slip from 'code' to 'information' and 'instruction'. The gene has a less content-full
and isolated role to play in the process of the cell than
these terms imply. Nevertheless, it has become a common-
place to state, in effect, that 'the genes carry the instructions which build the proteins which, in turn, build an
organism', so that the organism is a direct result of genetic
programmes, instructions, and commands. DNA is regarded
as supplying a very specific and detailed set of instructions
for the activation and control of the chemical processes of
life. It is this which allows people to put genes at the centre
of the story of life — as the controlling character determining the outcome of the plot — and to speak of 'the selfish
gene'. The metaphor may be mistaken, but strong theories
of gene-culture coevolution have been built on it. So how
does the argument develop?

Fundamental to all theories of evolution is the balance
achieved in organic life between stability and change. What
is known as 'mitosis' describes the process of cell division
which is the source of new cells in growth and development,
and wherever cell replacement is necessary. During mitosis, sets of enzymes ensure extremely accurate copying of
the DNA of the parent cell to provide the two consequent
cells with a full complement of DNA.

'Gene expression' describes the process whereby DNA
sequences (genes) are used to construct specific intermediate molecules which direct protein synthesis in specialized
sites in the cell, known as 'ribosomes'. These intermediate
molecules are examples of messenger RNA, which, in conjunction with transfer RNA and specialized enzymes at the

ribosome sites, produce chains of amino acids called 'polypeptides'.

These polypeptides turn and twist and fold into three-dimensional configurations and go on to form, where appropriate, enzymes and other proteins. About seven hundred proteins are then assembled into the components of the many different structures and substances of the body. In oversimplified and pictorial form, the process is often likened to that of a factory: DNA supplies the blueprint; messenger RNA carries the blueprint to the working site of the ribosomes; transfer RNA carries the assembly-line activity into the final product, the protein.

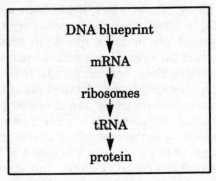

DNA blueprint
↓
mRNA
↓
ribosomes
↓
tRNA
↓
protein

Genes, therefore, specify what the constitution of the protein molecules will be; other parts of the gene form part of the means by which the production of proteins is turned on and off, forming a part of the signalling system which responds to the environment in turning protein manufacture off and on as required; and they serve as a pattern for the making of further copies of themselves. *None of this can be done in isolation*: genes are a part of a process in which no part is more or less important than the other parts. Despite this, genes are often described as though they are agents of their own or of other activity. Thus, genes are described as making proteins (frequently in the short-hand formula, genes make proteins that make bodies) or as being self-replicating. Nothing could be more erroneous, though, as we shall see, it is an error that underlies Richard Dawkins' account of the selfish gene. It is a fundamental mistake to make genes into purposive agents of activity. They are not. They are part of a complicated process in which many parts are equally important.

At the moment, we need simply to register the point in order to remind ourselves later of the further errors that surge in when genes are personified as purposive agents of activity, and when they are isolated from the entire developmental process in which they are embedded. We also need to follow the argument further, which has led to the proposal of Sociobiology as a theory, by establishing the distinction between genotype and phenotype, between the genetic constitution of an individual and the observable characteristics of the actual person.

Neo-Darwinian orthodoxy regards evolution as proceeding by the differential reproduction of hereditary characteristics by a process of natural selection. That is to say, the variations between individuals which natural selection operates on are attributed largely to genetic differences between individuals, which, in gene expression, produce different phenotypes, that is, different observable traits of structure and function in particular individuals.

What, then, are the *sources* of these genetic differences between individuals? The answer lies in the fertilized egg, which receives half of its chromosomes from the father and half from the mother, situated in the sperm and ovum respectively. 'Chromosomes' are protein strands in which genes are embedded. Each chromosome contains a characteristic set of genes, with the positions of each gene relatively fixed. One source of genetic variation is that one of a set of variants of a gene ('alleles') may occupy a given chromosomal site ('locus'). As there are many thousands of such loci, it is vastly improbable that any two individuals could have exactly the same genes on any given chromosome (with the exception of identical twins) if (as it does) a mechanism exists to assemble randomly unique sequences of alleles.

This mechanism is the process of 'meiosis', which produces the male and female sex cells. During the formation of sex cells, a random process of exchange of genetic material between paired chromosomes occurs prior to the separation of the chromosomes into the single sets contained in each sex cell. In other words, genetic recombination in meiosis ensures that each of the twenty-three single chromosomes in a human sex cell contains a unique combination of alleles. This greatly enhances the genetic diversity of offspring. As Loren Eisley put it, 'Whenever an infant is born, the dice . . . are being rolled again. Each one of us is a statistical impossibility, around which hover a million other lives that were never destined to be born.' The unique genetic constitution of an individual is referred to as its 'genotype'. The 'phenotype' is the appearance of, and the characteristics present in, an organism, which are a consequence of the interaction between the genetic constitution and the environment in which development occurs.

The distinction between genotype and phenotype gives culture its opportunity to influence the developmental process, and the distinction is thus vital for theories of gene-culture coevolution. To see how important it is, let us return to Mr Furman (p. 9) and his world record for forward somersaulting. The enormous muscular hypertrophy that such an achievement requires undoubtedly demands active and sustained gene expression within his muscle cells, but it also demands a culturally organized regimen of exercise — '. . . on a running track in the middle of the night . . .' — without which the necessary muscular development could not have occurred. Beyond this, some athletes (for example, weightlifters) have discovered the effect on muscular development of anabolic steroids. This again is an input from the cultural environment, and one that a cultural invention — of Sports' Councils — has attempted to control. Thus, any phenotype, including that of Mr Furman, is a consequence of gene expression and cultural context — in his case, that of exercise.

Thus, the distinction between genotype and phenotype lies in the fact that the process to which genes contribute does not build the observable phenotypic consequences in an exclusive and absolutely predictable way. Genes are a part of the process that produces proteins, which, in turn, form the structures and substances of our bodies, including our muscles. However, Mr Furman (and anybody else) can alter the phenotypical expression of his or her muscles by taking exercise. On the other hand, the reverse cannot happen: what is known as 'the Central Dogma' of protein synthesis states that '. . . once "information" has passed into protein *it cannot get out again'* (F. Crick, *What Mad Pursuit: A Personal View of Scientific Discovery*, London, Weidenfeld, 1988, p. 109). This means that acquired characteristics, like Mr Furman's enhanced muscles, cannot get back into the genome. To put it more generally, cultural achievements, however advantageous in protecting the replication of genetic information, cannot work back directly into a modification of the genes. The distinction is fundamental to theories of gene-culture coevolution, as Pulliam and Dunford make clear:

> With the advent of social learning, the evolution of behaviour begins to run on two tracks, genetic and cultural, which are interdependent but nevertheless separable. Both genetic and cultural evolution depend on transmission of information from one generation to the next. Genetic transmission is by reproduction. Cultural transmission is by learning from others . . . . A genetic trait spreads in a population because it enhances relative fitness: is the same true of a cultural trait?
>
> H. R. Pulliam and C. Dunford, *Programmed to Learn: An Essay on the Evolution of Culture* (New York, Columbia University Press, 1980), p. 8.

Strong Theories of gene-culture coevolution answer this last question in the affirmative; Weak Theories answer it by saying, 'Perhaps, but only in some, certainly not in all, cases'. What does this mean?

Let us return for a moment to Mr Furman on his pogo stick in the deep end. Strong Theories of gene-culture coevolution claim that his genes channel his interests and behaviours as a result of their effects on the development of his body and brain. These interests and behaviours — expressed, for example, in the invention of new exercises — may affect the success with which he replicates his genes. Strong Theories would go on to claim that such inventions will be culturally stabilized if they enhance the probability of gene-replication in the case of Mr Furman and his descendants, who, by virtue of their genetic and cultural inheritance, are more likely to acquire their ancestor's inventions than their reproductive competitors.

What this means, if we continue with the case of aqua-pogoing, is that the exploration of new environments is limited by the conditions set by survival: he needs his snorkel. But the development of muscles required for this novel activity, plus the fact that the cultural invention of the snorkel opens up new environments in which survival is possible, outweighs the risks involved — of drowning or of breaking his neck. There is now a better chance that the genetic information which built him (as Strong Theories would phrase it) will be replicated into another generation. Even so, the necessary muscles that make it possible for him to engage in this activity cannot be translated back into modified genes — aqua-pogoing is a cultural achievement that has to be learned (though learning ability, on this view, is under strong genetic constraint). Thus, Strong Theories of gene-culture coevolution argue that successful and long-running cultural inventions are those that protect the organism and enhance the probability of gene-replication, whilst being initially generated, and then relearned in subsequent generations via cognitive biases developing under strong genetic constraints.

Those who emphasize the independence of culture, however, argue that the invention of aqua-pogoing has more to do with the promotion of cultural 'crazes' and with earning money than with gene replication. Of course, such crazes will often be linked to sex, especially if they reach the stage of being advertised; but even sex has increasingly little to do with gene-replication in technologically protected societies. Walking on hot coals may lead to sex, but not necessarily to gene-replication, which, in any case, is now so much more planned that it leaves *space* for the independence of culture. Weak Theories, therefore, do not accept that cultural traits spread because they enhance relative fitness; they spread because, for example, they are fun — there are cultural reasons for cultural survival.

However, both Strong and Weak Theories agree in their recognition of two qualities of the gene which have major implications for culture and which are summarized in the two phrases, 'the immortal gene' and 'the selfish gene'. We can follow the debate further if we see what is meant by these phrases.

3

The Immortal Gene and the Selfish Gene

'The immortal gene' is a recognition of the stability of gene-coding, that the three-base code for each amino acid remains stable. This means that every living organism, from the simplest bacteriophage to human beings, uses an identical set of triplet codons to translate the base sequence of messenger RNA to the amino acid sequence of a polypeptide chain. So, to give an example, a codon AUG universally specifies methionine, and UUU universally specifies phenylalanine. Commenting on this, Suso Ohno has argued that the codons are universal, not because the triplet coding system represents the ideal solution to the problem, but because the very first replicating nucleic acid, which was formed many millions of years ago, was constrained into the coding system because it happened to be able to do the job. Once this had happened, at the very beginning of life, the coding system had to be preserved. As Ohno put it:

Once the coding system was established, at the very beginning of life, there was no choice but to conserve it *in toto* in all the myriad descendants of that first creature. Any subsequent attempt to change the coding system would necessarily have made a mockery of all previous messages that were encoded within the DNA, thus resulting in the immediate extermination of any organism which dared to attempt a change. In this manner, all organisms are bound to the past. As they evolve, their past history becomes an increasing

28

burden which progressively restricts their future evolutionary possibilities. As hard as modern man strives to be free
he is a slave chained to the past.
> 'The Development of Sexual Reproduction', in C. R. Austin
> and R. V. Short, *The Evolution of Reproduction*
> (Cambridge University Press, 1976) p. 22.

Of course, it is a provisional sense of immortality, as it is
not exempt from the destruction of all DNA in some entire
global catastrophe. Nevertheless, this provisional immortality has been described very effectively by Macfarlane
Burnett:

> For someone still with a capacity for wonder, it can be fasci-
> nating to look through a microscope at one of his own white
> blood cells. He can see the round central nucleus and he
> knows that in the nucleus are strands of DNA. It is the lit-
> eral truth that the patterned molecules in that DNA have
> come down in an immortal, unbroken sequence for 3000
> million years from the single micro-organism within which
> the universal genetic code first took its definitive form. Life
> in that sense is immortal, and in the early stages, when
> reproduction was no more than growth and division into
> two, there was no immediate biological necessity for death.
> *The Endurance of Life: The implications of genetics for*
> *human life* (Cambridge University Press, 1978) p. 7.

Genetic instructions, therefore, are extremely stable and
long-running — so much so that Eigen regarded the challenge to evolutionary theory to be the explanation, not of
change, but of how stability is achieved (see, e.g., *The
Hypercycle: A principle of natural self-organisation* (Berlin,
Springer-Verlag, 1979) p. 7). But then we may well ask
how *any* change comes about. The major mechanisms are
mutation, recombination, and self-engineering. They are
assisted by gene flow and genetic drift. All these, in different ways, have implications for theories of gene-culture
coevolution.

Mutations are physical changes in genes which, if they
are not simply destructive, alter the gene's effects. Mutations are lasting chemical changes in the sequences of
nucleotide subunits of DNA. They are brought about by the

replacement of one nucleotide by another of a different kind (a 'point mutation') or by inversions, deletions and translocations of whole regions of chromosomes. Once the nucleotide sequence is changed, the polypeptides synthesized from the mutated DNA may also change. Such changes may be disastrous to the organism, which would mean that the mutation is not replicated into future generations. On the other hand, the mutation may be neutral (or neutral with potential benefit when combined with other yet-to-come mutations) or advantageous. Mutations may be on a small scale, but homeotic mutations are those that involve large areas. For example, when the homeotic selector genes of fruit flies have been mutated in experimental conditions, eyes have grown into legs and antennae into wings. So, mutations may occur by chance and at random or they may be induced in the environment chemically or by radiation. However it is caused, though, either a mutation will help an organism to survive and replicate that genetic information, or it will be neutral, or it will be disadvantageous and will disappear.

Mutations provide the raw material of evolution, understood as stable organizations of energy open to transmissible, and thus inheritable, change. The impartial judge of success or failure is natural selection — the selection of those mutations fit to survive. Also important in this evolutionary movement (as indicated earlier, pp. 23–4) is 'recombination' — the generation of new combinations of genes during meiosis — as then material is randomly exchanged between maternal and paternal chromosomes. Mutations, which may include the deletion of genetic material, can occur in this process.

Genetic evolution is then affected in a different way by gene flow and genetic drift. 'Gene flow' arises from migration to and from different regions and populations. 'Genetic drift', which is sometimes also referred to as 'sampling error', is the process whereby genetic instructions controlling particular items are lost from a population by not being transmitted from parents to offspring. It arises from the chance events of gene transmission in finite populations — usually small and isolated populations — because in large populations, any specific trait is carried by so many individuals that its loss (unless it is highly unfavourable) is unlikely. The fact that blood group B is almost completely absent among American Indians is sometimes claimed to be an example of genetic drift.

In these ways, mutations, recombination and self-engineering will alter the genetic instructions and will thus alter what is built; gene flow (and, to a lesser degree, genetic drift) will open up new combinations of genetic information. Locked on to Darwin and Mendel, this means that the transmissible variations will either, eventually, help an organism to survive or they will not. Helpful mutations are those which enable an organism to survive more effectively in the competition for resources and mates, and, thus, to replicate its genes into another generation. 'Survival of the survivors' therefore becomes a tautological definition of 'survival of the fittest': the fittest are simply those who happen to survive.

This abbreviated account makes it possible now to understand what is meant by the phrase 'the selfish gene'. Suppose we tell the same story from the viewpoint of the gene — assuming, for the moment, that the gene could have a view and could have intentions or purpose. Genes are, as we have seen, molecules built in such a way that they can be replicated and transmitted from one organism to another; while this is being done, they have no awareness of, or concern for, the experience of the organism. But, from the genes' point of view, the bodies they inhabit can be regarded as 'space capsules' constructed for their own survival, so that any organism can be regarded as a gene-survival machine. Samuel Butler put the point succinctly when he observed that a chicken is an egg's way of making another egg. We can, of course, unpack this brief definition, as Borek does:

A fertilized egg is at once the most precious and the most baffling thing in the universe. Within the thin shell of a hen's egg is locked not just a mere mass of egg white and

yolk, but a promise of a beautiful creature of flesh, blood
and bones — a promise of the continuity of life.

> E. Borek, *The Atoms Within Us* (New York,
> Colombia University Press, 1980) p. 1.

From the gene's perspective, the point is not the beauty but
the continuity of life: either the genes are replicated or they
are not. If they are not, then that line of transmission comes
to a halt. The gene is only 'concerned' with the continuity of
its own sequence, not with the experience of particular
organisms — hence the phrase 'the selfish gene'.

This phrase, it should be noted, has another, more technical, meaning. The amount of DNA in organisms is more
than is used, or apparently required, to build them. Much
of the DNA in human cells has no known purpose. It looks
as though at least some of it is redundant, and is simply
going along for the ride. This is called 'selfish' DNA (it is
serving no purpose other than its own replication) in a
slightly different sense and is, therefore, sometimes also
called 'junk' or nonsense DNA, though, in fact, it is no different functionally from the 'useful' DNA, in the sense that
both are simply saying 'transmit me'. Nevertheless, it would
make sense to regard the additional DNA as benignly
parasitic on the DNA committed to the construction of the
survival machine, so in this sense, again, it is 'selfish' (see
the review article, W. F. Doolittle and C. Sapienza 'Selfish
Genes, the Phenotype Paradigm and Genome Evolution',
Nature, 284, no. 5757, 1980, pp. 601–7).

The selfish gene is not *so* selfish that it has to replicate
itself precisely or otherwise face extinction. Related copies
of the genes are carried by exactly these — near relatives.
It is this consideration which supplies one part of the
answer to John Turner's questions:

> How could natural selection explain a creature that often
> behaved with such moral fortitude and such disregard for
> its own individual survival? What gorilla would let itself be
> burned alive for the sake of denying that bread was flesh or
> flesh bread? What chimpanzee would sink in its thousands
> in the mud of Passchendaele for Kaiser, king and country?
>
> *New Scientist*, 9 February, 1984, p. 34.

His questions had been partly answered by Trivers and Hamilton in 1963. Using the insights of population genetics, they argued that it is not the genes of the individual which have to survive, but, rather, the *related* genes of the *kinship group*. In fact, the gene-programmed sacrifice of *some* individuals (for example, in defence of a nest or hive) may enhance the probability of other members of the kinship group surviving. In this way, kinship altruism is rewarded by kin selection, and this can be explained along straightforward neo-Darwinian lines, provided that the altruism is not too extensively self-sacrificing, and provided that it is expended on close enough relatives. It was this which led to the famous remark by Haldane, 'Greater love hath no man than this, that he lay down his life for two brothers, four half brothers or eight first cousins'.

However, this line of thought on its own would not explain altruism on behalf of one's country (an extremely wide gene-pool in most instances) or, in the case of celibacy, on behalf of the whole human race; nor would it explain why people give generously to famine or disaster appeals when it is strictly in their own (gene-replication) interest to reduce demand on finite resources. If there are too many people in the lifeboat, the strongest would improve their own chances of survival by pushing the weakest over the side — or, for that matter, eating them, as with the crew of the 'Nancy Bell', or as Japanese soldiers did with prisoners of war at the end of the Second World War (*The Daily Telegraph*, 12 August, 1992, p. 9, reporting the archive research of Toshiyuki Tanaka). Trivers therefore argued that 'reciprocal altruism' (i.e., the evolution of reproductive sacrifice in a species) *can* be rewarded in genetic selection *provided* that there is an eventual (even if only theoretical) net return benefit:

> One human being saving another, who is not closely related and is about to drown, is an instance of altruism. Assume that the chance of the drowning man dying is one-half if no one leaps in to save him, but the chance that his potential rescuer will drown if he leaps in to save him is much smaller, say, one in twenty. Assume that the drowning man always

drowns when his rescuer does and that he is always saved
when the rescuer survives the rescue attempt . . . . Were
this an isolated event, it is clear that the rescuer should not
bother to save the drowning man. But if the drowning man
reciprocates at some future time, and if the survival chances
are then exactly reversed, it will have been to the benefit of
each participant to have risked his life for the other . . . . If
we assume that the entire population is sooner or later
exposed to the same risk of drowning, the two individuals
who rescue each other will be selected over those who face
drowning on their own.

> R. L. Trivers, 'The evolution of reciprocal altruism',
> *Quarterly Review of Biology*, XLVI, 1971, p. 36.

It is here that the foundations of sociobiology are laid: if
genes build proteins which build bodies and brains (to
adopt for the moment, this misleading formula) in such a
way that they engage in social behaviour — in this case,
reciprocal altruism — then this confers an adaptive advantage on its bearers that will be differentially reproduced in
successive generations. In point of fact, it is by no means
certain that the key developmental interactants maintaining
such adaptive social behaviours are genes, but sociobiologists have tended to argue that this is the case. While it is
true that units of evolution must be heritable replicators,
open to (mainly) gradual change, units of selection may be
genes, gene-complexes, genomes, organisms, populations
or species, as the title of a recent collection makes clear:
*Genes, Organisms, Populations: Controversies Over the Units
of Selection* (R. N. Brandon and R. M. Burian, eds,
Cambridge, MIT Press, 1987). In principle, genes are not
the only replicators. As we shall see, most theories of gene-
culture coevolution now assume that cultural items also
replicate themselves by means of human brains, as parallel
systems of information processing. It is a mark of Weak
Theories of gene-culture coevolution that cultural replicators
are at least to some extent decoupled from gene-replication
where Darwinian survival or fitness is concerned. It is a
mark of Strong Theories of gene-culture coevolution that
they accord strong causal primacy to the genes in deter-

mining survival and fitness: for them, it is gene-continuity that is the measure of fitness.

Strong theories of gene-culture coevolution: Sociobiology Mark I

Among the Strong Theories, it is Sociobiology which has been the pioneering enterprise. Although Sociobiology has itself changed during the years of argument and debate, we need to track back into what we may call 'Sociobiology Mark I' in order to understand how the argument has built up that God is a virus. Sociobiology Mark I appeared in E. O. Wilson's *Sociobiology: The new synthesis* (1975), and, at a more popular level, in his *On Human Nature* (1978), and in such other works as D. P. Barash's *Sociobiology and Behaviour* (1977) and his *Whisperings Within: Evolution and the origins of human nature* (1979).

In Sociobiology Mark I, the linkage between genes and culture is so close that genes can be regarded as a fundamental cause of culture. To put the argument as briefly as possible (although the form of the argument is expressed in terms which, as we have begun to see, are strictly inaccurate), genes build bodies, through which the information that they hold is protected until it can be replicated in another generation. Anything, including culture, which helps to protect the bodies long enough to replicate the genetic information, and which then protects the offspring long enough to continue the process, will be rewarded in natural selection by survival. The proof of the pudding is in the breeding. A cultural belief is then a conscious interpretation of a genetic endowment or demand, the articulated message of what Barash called 'the whisperings within'. The genes sit within the boundary of the skin which protects them (all being well) long enough for them to replicate themselves into another generation. Culture is the second defensive skin within which the genes sit.

So, we arrive at what Wilson called

. . . the heart of the genetic hypothesis, . . . the proposition, derived in a straight line from neo-Darwinian evolutionary

theory, that the traits of human nature were adaptive during the time that the human species evolved and that genes
consequently spread through the population that predis-
posed their carriers to develop those traits: adaptiveness
means simply that if an individual displayed the traits he
stood a greater chance of having his genes represented in
the next generation than if he did not display the traits; the
differential advantage among individuals in this strictest
sense is called genetic fitness.

On Human Nature, p. 32.

From this perspective, Wilson derived a picture of human
development in which '. . . the newly fertilised egg, a cor-
puscle one two-hundredth of an inch in diameter, is not a
human being: it is a set of instructions sent floating into
the cavity of the womb . . .' (p. 53). Among these instructions are those which initiate and control the wiring of
neurons in the brain. The question then becomes, '. . . to
what extent does the wiring of the neurons, so undeniably
encoded in the genes, preordain the directions that social
development will follow?' (p. 55). The answer is, 'not as
restrictedly as in the case of an insect, but within limits
nevertheless':

The channels of human mental development, in contrast [to
a mosquito], are circuitous and variable: rather than specify
a single trait, human genes prescribe the *capacity* to develop
a certain array of traits; in some categories of behavior, the
array is limited and the outcome can be altered only by
strenuous training [e.g., left-handedness] — if ever. In
others, the array is vast and the outcome easily influenced.

pp. 56ff.

It is thus not the case that there is only one, single cultural
outcome in the human case, but, rather, that there is a
range of ways in which the controlling predisposition of the
genes can be satisfied. Only time can tell, by the straightforward test of survival and gene-replication, which cultural
solutions are most adaptive (in the sense of adaptiveness
above).

4

Sociobiology and Religion

On this basis, Wilson was able to launch his analysis of religion, which carried with it a secular crusade against God. For Wilson, religion is the greatest challenge to Sociobiology: 'Religion constitutes the greatest challenge to human Sociobiology and its most exciting opportunity to progress as a truly original theoretical discipline' (*On Human Nature*, p. 175). Wilson unfolds a paradox: on the one hand, 'the predisposition to religious belief is the most complex and powerful force in the human mind and in all probability an ineradicable part of human nature' (p. 169); on the other hand, it rests on 'an unthinking submission to the communal will' (p. 184) — with all the adaptive advantages that this confers, but with all the lamentable history of religions as well — and on myths which are now known to be absurd and false. Myths are 'the narratives by which the tribe's special place in the world is explained in rational terms consistent with the listener's understanding of the physical world' (p. 189). Religion, therefore, persists in a world in which scientific materialism has exposed the error of its foundational stories: 'Scientific materialism presents the human mind with an alternative mythology that until now has always, point for point in zones of conflict, defeated traditional religion' (p. 192).

How, then, can Sociobiology meet its greatest challenge and account for the deeply embedded persistence of religion even when its articulated foundations are shown to be full of error? The answer, in Wilson's view, is that the genes

37

created the capacity for those elements of behaviour which we call 'religious', and that the choice of some (as opposed to others) has rewarded and protected those genes which predispose individuals to conform. Particular religious rituals or other practices may vary in detail, and are thus 'chosen' by what Wilson calls 'ecclesiastic selection' at the level of cultural learning, but all the time the frequencies of genes are changing. So Wilson argued:

> The hypothesis before us is that some gene frequencies are changed in consistent ways by ecclesiastic selection. Human genes, it will be recalled, program the functioning of the nervous, sensory, and hormonal systems of the body, and thereby almost certainly influence the learning process. They constrain the maturation of some behaviors and the learning rules of other behaviors. Incest taboos, taboos in general, xenophobia, the dichotomization of objects into the sacred and profane, nosism, hierarchical dominance systems, intense attention towards leaders, charisma, trophyism, and trance-induction are among the elements of religious behavior most likely to be shaped by developmental programs and learning rules. All of these processes act to circumscribe a social group and bind its members together in unquestioning allegiance. Our hypothesis requires that such constraints exist, that they have a physiological basis, and that the physiological basis in turn has a genetic origin. It implies that ecclesiastical choices are influenced by the chain of events that lead from the genes through physiology to constrained learning during single lifetimes.
>
> According to the hypothesis, the frequencies of the genes themselves are reciprocally altered by the descending sequence of several kinds of selection — ecclesiastic, ecological, and genetic — over many lifetimes. Religious practices that consistently enhance survival and procreation of the practitioners will propagate the physiological controls that favor acquisition of the practices during single lifetimes. The genes that prescribe the controls will also be favored.
>
> p. 177.

Looking at the religious world, one is inevitably impressed by the prolific diversity of the religious imagination. As I once summarized the point:

What then does it mean to be religiously human? It means sacrificing lambs and goats — and occasionally human beings as well; it means building Chartres cathedral, the Golden Pagoda of the Buddha, and the Great Pyramid; it means praying, meditating, levitating, worshipping, withdrawing into silence, and speaking with tongues; it means being baptized, being circumcised, never cutting one's hair, and having one's head shaved; it means crossing oceans and continents on pilgrimage, in missionary endeavor, for the fighting of jihads or for crusades or for holy wars; it means loving one's neighbor as oneself and excommunicating him to a fate far worse than death; it means the inspired creation of music, art, icons, symbols, poetry at the very furthest stretch of the human imagination, and yet it also means banal sentiment and what Rose Macaulay once called 'bleeding hearts in convent parlours'; it means having a soul and not having a soul; it means faith, martyrdom, hypocrisy, vindictive cruelty, self-sacrificing love. It means virtually everything, for religion represents both the means and the product of the human animal's deepest and most extensive search for its own meaning, for the truth and destiny of its own nature and of the universe in which its life is at present set. How can we even begin to grasp and understand something so vast that it embraces virtually the whole of everything?

Zygon, XVI, 1981, p. 366.

Wilson's claim is that *only* sociobiology can account for such diversity: religions are protective systems which change gene-frequencies and which enhance the probability of gene-replication. It is of little consequence that religions promote beliefs which, from a rational point of view, appear, at least to some, to be absurd or false. The issue is whether these beliefs have proved to be effective in sustaining systems that have protected gene-replication. Clearly they have. The value of religions as protective systems for gene-replication and the nurture of children is dramatically obvious in the preoccupation which all long-running religions display, with sex and food. To take only one brief example, Islam is a highly formal information system, supplying guidance for human behaviours from the Qur'an. The

Qur'an is affirmed as revelation from God, which is then explicated in *shari'a*, the applied law codes. In al-Qaradawi's guide to 'the lawful and the prohibited in Islam' (to follow the title of his book, American Trust Publications, n.d.), 42 per cent of the material is concerned with sexual matters and with food, with a further 6 per cent being concerned with dress and personal appearance. 'God' (i.e., belief in God) is a powerful sanction and promise, reinforcing controls over behaviour.

It is because religions have been so successful that, in Wilson's view, they are likely to continue, even though theology as a human intellectual discipline will disappear as completely as alchemy because it has no rational foundation. That is, religions will survive for some time (because they are long-running and well-tested systems for the protection of genetic information), but theology is finished (because its cognitive claims about God are an articulated interpretation of the 'whisperings within', the truth-value of which has been shown, on other grounds, to be exhausted):

> If this interpretation [sc., Sociobiology] is correct, the final decisive edge enjoyed by scientific naturalism will come from its capacity to explain traditional religion, its chief competitor, as a wholly material phenomenon. Theology is not likely to survive as an independent intellectual discipline. But religion itself will endure for a long time as a vital force in society.
>
> *On Human Nature*, p. 192.

Culture and genes — dependence or independence?

From this analysis of culture as a protective system, it follows, for Sociobiology Mark I, that culture is simply part of the environment with which genes interact as they 'search' for contexts that will enhance the probability of their own replication. Culture is *not* a detached information system following a history of its own, unrelated to the consequence of genetic fitness. As Flinn and Alexander put the point strongly, '. . . no rationale has ever been advanced for regarding the influence of culture on the development and expression of behaviour as other than a special subset of the environment' (M. V. Flinn and R. D. Alexander, 'Culture theory: the developing synthesis from biology', *Human Ecology* X, 1982, p. 391). At an extreme, this could mean that cultural items are not regarded as independent replicators at all. As Alexander argued, there would be every reason to expect a correlation between culture change and the maximization of inclusive fitness (i.e., on this view, culture *only* changes if such changes serve the purpose of the genes):

> To whatever extent the use of culture by individuals is learned — and if this is not the rule then one is at a loss to explain how any special human capacity to use and transmit culture could have evolved — *regularity of learning situations or environmental consistency is the link between genetic instructions and cultural instructions which makes the latter not a replicator at all, but in historical terms, a vehicle of the genetic replicators.*
>
> R. D. Alexander, *Darwinism and Human Affairs*
> (Seattle, University of Washington, 1979) p. 79.

On this view, the genes differentially constrain brain development to channel perception, cognition, emotion and behaviour into adaptive forms that are codified and reinforced through symbolic representation in culture. The forms of behaviour and their cultural codification that are preserved through time are those which protect the genes constraining the development of their bases in brain structure and function.

However, supposing the brain develops so that it can evaluate its perceptions, cognitions and behaviours on grounds other than those of survival fitness for the genes: then, first, it must still be *linked* to that survival fitness (otherwise the hardware would go to extinction), but, second, it may *additionally* perpetuate cultural achievements, irrespective of survival fitness, for cultural reasons. It might, for example, perpetuate them because they are perceived to be true, beautiful, or good, to quote the traditional triad of values. By coincidence, 'the true' might enhance the probability of gene-replication, but it might equally be

inimical to it. The consequence would be a relatively independent history of cultural transmission in which the survival fitness of cultural traits would have to be separately
considered. In other words, exactly as Cavalli-Sforza and
Feldman argued, there would be two kinds of fitness in
culture-bearing populations, in which 'the probability of
acceptance as a measure of *cultural selection* must be clearly
differentiated from the *Darwinian* or *natural selection* due
to the cultural trait' (L. L. Cavalli-Sforza and M. W.
Feldman, *Cultural Transmission and Evolution*, Princeton,
University Press, 1981, pp. 15ff.).

If we return once more to the New York pool (p. 9), the
distinction becomes clear. Mr Furman is held within limits
of survival: he devised equipment which would not only
enable him to live in the strange environment of the deep
end, but also give him an adaptive advantage in the event
of another great flood. Again, his somersaulting enhanced
his agility, so that he would have greater chances of escape
if, in the park at midnight, he had been threatened with a
mugging. He has used both brain and body for the purposes
of cultural invention, not necessarily *in order to* enhance
the probability of gene-replication, but in ways that have
increased this probability nonetheless. Yet, to go on somersaulting through the night in order to beat the world record,
or to use this skill in order to entertain children, or to find
a game that might lead to commercial success, is to move
into a different world of evaluation. It may be *linked* to
Darwinian fitness, but it has acquired cultural fitness as
well.

Two worlds: the operational and the cognized environments of human life

The point is that humans live in two worlds at once. There
is a given world of context — a world of constraints and
opportunities, a world which we tend to refer to in terms of
natural law, or at least of predictable recurrence, a world of
oxygen requirements, gravity, pressure, metabolism, gene
transcription, and the like — but humans live also in that

world of context as they experience it, and, at no time, not even in the present, does the experienced world give an exact description or account of 'the world as it really is'. We construct our experienced worlds in very different ways, and it is a fundamental mistake to suppose that an experienced world only has value if it serves the purposes of Darwinian fitness. It may have developed values, satisfactions and entertainments of its own.

These last considerations are already moving us in the direction of a Weak Theory of gene-culture coevolution. They accept the distinction drawn by Rappoport between the environment in which an organism lives (the operational environment, or Eo) and the mental perception and conception of this environment and of the events that occur within it (the cognized environment, or Ec). A sociobiologist, or any other behavioural observer, sees the cultural context as the operational environment (in which the work of the genes is going on, even though the participants in that culture may happen to be unaware of it), but the cognized environment is the one in which people live their enculturated lives. However, in contrast to sociobiology, the Rappoport distinction means that, while the two environments, Eo and Ec, may indeed overlap (in the sense that what a population perceives to be the case in their environment correlates well with what an outside observer, in a different frame of reference, might report as occurring within it), frequently they do not. In that case, the Ec may be independent of the Eo, and, indeed, in conceptual conflict with it. Thus Rappoport argues:

> The operational model of the environment is that which the anthropologist constructs through observation and measurement of empirical entities, events and material relationships. He takes this model to represent, for analytical purposes, the physical world of the group he is studying . . . . The cognized model is the model of the environment conceived by the people who act in it. The two models are overlapping but not identical. While many components of the physical world will be represented in both, the operational model is likely to include material elements, such as disease germs

and nitrogen-fixing bacteria, that affect the actors but of which they are not aware. Conversely, the cognized model may include elements that cannot be shown by empirical means to exist, such as spirits and other supernatural beings.

A. R. Rappoport, *Pigs for Ancestors* (New Haven, Yale University Press, 1968) pp. 237f.

Three important points need to be made. First, there is no privileged Ec that can adjudicate on the truth or value of other Ecs: it can only do so on its own terms of reference. Anthropologists/sociobiologists do not possess the *only* canon of truth, since their conceptualizations are one Ec among many. In contrast to the assumption that the Eo can be determined from the privileged vantage point of the scientific observer, what is being argued here is that an observer's specification of the world which an observed people inhabits is *itself* an Ec. Second, it follows that the languages, symbols, and so on, by means of which an Ec is expressed, are never a direct, infallible representation of Eo — not even if they are called 'sociobiology' (there is no way in which human language or representation in non-linguistic form can directly deliver, without interpretation, what it purports to be about). Third, the approximate nature of all human articulations of Ec means that they cannot be decoded for meaning or for value against one particular and privileged Ec (say, that of a sociobiologist) as though that alone has a truth-value, but have to be assessed, at least initially, for truth, interest and value in relation to their own contextual system. Thus, the language of supernatural beings is, necessarily, a way of articulating in an Ec a perception of the Eo in which a culture happens to be set. *What* is being claimed in Ec 1 (say, Orthodox Judaism) is by no means automatically what *seems* to be being claimed through that language in the conceptual scheme of Ec 2 (i.e., 'supernatural being' in Ec 1 will have vastly different contextual associations in Ec 2 and will, therefore, 'mean' something different in each system; the implications of this for hermeneutics are discussed more fully in Part III). One cannot legitimately use the values of

Ec 2 to claim the evident absurdity of the belief in 'super-natural beings' in Ec 1. The translation programme between the two, if indeed it were feasible, would require careful and public exposition.

These considerations are leading (as they have led many anthropologists in the twentieth century) in the direction of cultural relativity — the claim that there is no Archimedean point (of independence from one's *own* acculturation) on which to stand in order to assess the truth or otherwise of the immensely varied descriptions or beliefs which occur in human cultures.

However, the movement in this relativizing direction is at least controlled by the recognition that the Eo — the universe as it happens to be — sets a limit on language, although language can never describe what it is that the universe happens to be. All our descriptive languages are approximate, provisional, corrigible, and mainly wrong — not least from the point of view of later generations. Never-theless, many of our languages (for example, of the natural sciences or of theology) achieve impressive reliability because the Eo does set a limit on feasible utterance. If this were not so, there could be no truth conditions of any kind, nor could there be transmissible or shareable culture because all events would then be random.

This recognition (which is discussed at greater length in my book, *Licensed Insanities*, London, Darton, Longman and Todd, 1987; U.S. title, *Is Anybody Out There?*, Westminster, Christian Classics, 1988) gives rise to 'critical realism' in its many different forms. Absolute realism would be the mistaken view that we could take a look at the universe — unencumbered with theories about it — and describe it 'exactly as it is'. Critical realism accepts that our languages are approximate, corrigible, provisional, and, frequently, wrong, but that they are wrong about *something* — however imperfectly this 'something' is able to be known. But, if that is true of the natural sciences (as it is), it is equally true, *mutatis mutandis*, of theology. This, though, at once suggests that both science and theology (though in vastly different ways, because of the differences in their subject matter) move corrigibly through time because they establish reliabilities, that is, ways to proceed that we can trust, even though this process corrects or extends the formulation or account we inherited. In other words, the truth-conditions of human utterance make it inevitable that the cultural creations of human minds will take on a life of their own. They are not winnowed simply by their survival fitness in relation to the genes; culture, as the construction of Ec in its interaction with Eo, will achieve consequences which are not dictated directly from one item only of the Eo — in the case of Sociobiology Mark I, from the genes.

5

Sociobiology Mark II

Sociobiology Mark II met the challenge of this potential decoupling of cultural from genetic transmission by searching for human universals embedded in the midst of cultural diversity, and by arguing that these point to the emergence of the human mind as being itself controlled by genetic demand. In other words, while it may be true that culture stretches out on a long leash from the genes, it will, in the end, still be sifted in terms of survival fitness for the genes, because (according to this view) culture is mediated by the human mind, and the mind is created from the genes. The argument, therefore, is that within the brain there are now gene-derived structures which impose epigenetic rules.

On this basis, Wilson and Lumsden looked back on the work that led to their book, *Genes, Mind and Culture* (Cambridge, Harvard University Press, 1981) and summarized its central claim:

> The conception that began to emerge is that genes and culture are held together by an elastic but unbreakable leash. As culture surges forward by means of innovation and the introduction of new ideas and artifacts from the outside, it is constrained and directed to some extent by the genes. At the same time, the pressure of cultural innovation affects the survival of the genes and ultimately alters the strength and torque of the genetic leash.
>
> C. J. Lumsden and E. O. Wilson, *Promethean Fire: Reflections on the origin of mind* (Cambridge, Harvard University Press, 1983) p. 60.

47

For this to be true, though, it would have to be shown how
the genes (which change extremely slowly) can track culture (which changes extremely fast) in such a way that
they keep culture on a leash. Wilson and Lumsden address
this problem directly by proposing 'the thousand year
rule' — in contrast to what they call 'the conventional view':

> The conventional view is that significant genetic evolution
> requires thousands of years and largely came to a halt in
> human populations 30,000 years ago or more, after which
> cultural evolution took over as virtually the sole agent of
> change.

In contrast, Wilson and Lumsden claim that fifty generations, or a thousand years, is sufficient for genetic evolution
to establish the rules guiding thought and behaviour, even
with only limited selection. They argue that even since the
introduction of agriculture, approximately ten thousand
years ago,

> time has been more than adequate for substantial coevolu-
> tion and the establishment of some degree of epigenetic bias
> in virtually every category of cultural behaviour.

The epigenetic rules are fundamental to this version of
Sociobiology Mark II. Epigenesis is a term used in general
for the succession of changes whereby an embryonic organism passes through more or less distinct stages, in which
new parts and organs appear that are not preformed (in
contrast to morphogenesis, which refers to the slow
acquisition of the characteristic form and function of an
individual). For Lumsden and Wilson, epigenesis is 'the
sum of all the interactions between the genes and the environment that create the distinctive traits of an organism'
(p. 71). Epigenetic rules are the gene-built preferences in
the brain for one cultural decision rather than another.
Instead of people being, as Chairman Mao supposed, a
beautiful blank piece of paper on which any story can be
written, humans are highly circumscribed by the constraints which the genes have built into the brains.

A key example, which is offered by Wilson and Lumsden
in order to illustrate this, is that of the way in which,

universally, people perceive colours and code them in cultures — this being a key example because it reverses the hitherto prevailing conclusions of anthropologists that colour perception and coding are culture-specific, without a genetic control. 'Light' is electromagnetic radiation to which eyes, including human eyes, are sensitive. Light radiations occupy a small part of the electromagnetic spectrum, between 400 and 770 nanometers. The human eye recognizes light of different wavelengths as being of different colours, moving through the spectrum from blue at the shorter end, through green and yellow, to red at the longer. However, it seemed clear to anthropologists and linguists that the descriptions of colour in different cultures did not follow these divisions within the spectrum, as they should have done if the genes had built colour recognition into the brain in a determinative way. In other words, cultures and languages had allocated colour terms idiosyncratically: it seemed that 'each language performs the coding of experience into sound in a unique manner, [so that] each language is semantically arbitrary relative to every other language' (B. Berlin and P. Kay, *Basic Colour Terms: Their universality and evolution*, Berkeley, University of California Press, 1969, p. 1). On the basis of a study of the colour-naming systems of about sixty American Indian groups, V. F. Ray had concluded that cultural relativity, unconstrained by natural predispositions, was dominant: 'I conclude that there is no such thing as "natural" division of the spectrum. The colour systems of man are not based upon psychological, physiological or anatomical factors. Each culture has taken the spectral continuum and has divided it upon a basis which is quite arbitrary except for pragmatic considerations' (V. F. Ray, 'Human color perception and behavioral response', *Transactions of the New York Academy of Science*, XVI, 1953, p. 104).

In fact, almost exactly the reverse is true. The subsequent work of Berlin and Kay established a high degree of *concordance* in languages regarding designating the boundaries of the basic colour terms in relation to the four primary colours; and even among those groups which have no colour vocabulary beyond 'dark' and 'light', the work of Eleanor Rosch showed that they learned colour vocabularies more adeptly if its reference was located on the primary colours. For Wilson and Lumsden (and many others), this indicates a gene-built bias to perceive and code colours, not on a continuous spectrum, but according to 'the beautiful illusion' of four discrete, primary colours.

In *Promethean Fire* (pp. 64ff.), Wilson and Lumsden located twelve instances where the near universal cultural consequences require, in their view, a genetic base if they are to be explained. Thus, the facial expressions by means of which any particular group of humans expresses such emotions as rage, happiness, surprise, or frustration can be picked out from photographs by any other group of humans with at least an 80 per cent degree of accuracy in the decoding process (see P. Ekman, *The Face of Man: Expressions of universal emotions in a New Guinea village*, New York, Garland, 1980). The consequences, for Darwinian fitness, in being able to decode with accuracy the moods, and thus, perhaps, the intentions, of others is obvious. The epigenetic rule in this case is confirmed by people with prosopagnosia, a brain disorder caused by lesions which (as the underlying Greek words giving rise to the name of this disorder indicate) leaves such people unable to recognize others by their faces, so that they are compelled to differentiate between those they encounter by their voices. However, they *are* able to recognize non-facial representations of those basic expressions — for example, aggressive gestures or shouting to convey anger.

Another clear example lies in the incest taboo. Sexual relations or marriage between siblings or near relatives has a high fitness cost, in the sense that it increases the chance that a recessive allele, with disadvantageous consequences for the phenotype, will appear in a homozygote individual — quite apart from the fact that genetic variation will be reduced; and so, not surprisingly, many other animals, which lack culture, have behaviour patterns that deter incest. The epigenetic rule in this case is inferred also from the fact that non-relatives are avoided as if they were siblings if they have been brought up in close proximity during the first six years of life. Even where culture has encouraged young people to marry despite such proximity, as in Israeli kibbutzim, exactly the opposite has happened. In one study of 2769 marriages of children raised in kibbutzim, for example, none were between men and women raised in the same kibbutz from birth.

Other examples are phobias (which are evoked by dangers of an ancient environment, such as snakes, spiders, and heights, and not by those of a modern environment, such as guns or electric power sockets); selective taste preferences among infants; anxiety of young children in the presence of strangers; preference for particular shapes of visible objects. In all these instances, the tendency for humans to make particular choices clearly precedes any instruction they could receive from the cultural context. In other words, such tendencies are viewed as being innate.

It now becomes clear that culture is being defined as the sum of choices made by individuals which are endorsed and, where appropriate, transmitted in human societies. For Lumsden and Wilson, clarifying this process is 'the first crucial step' which leads to the isolation of cultural items of choice, called by them 'culturgens':

> The crucial first step is to examine the process that leads from the making of individual decisions to the formation of culture. At this level men manufacture their own history. Free will appears to be in charge. As Engels observed, 'Each person follows his own consciously desired end, and it is precisely the resultant of these many wills operating in different directions and of their manifold effects upon the outer world that constitutes history.' We approached the mind-to-culture translation with the aid of a proven rule of scientific research: theories are most easily constructed and understood if they manipulate discrete elements. Atoms, molecules, and genes are examples of such units that appear to be real and discrete. Populations, species, and ecosystems are units that are often arbitrary in their limits, but invaluable to science nonetheless. Human cultures consist of artifacts, such as knives of a certain shape and

function; behaviors, such as initiation rites of a particular
form; and mental constructions having little or no direct
correspondence to reality, such as myths. The findings of
anthropologists suggest that these units interact to form
larger coherent wholes.

After a careful examination of this evidence, we realized
that such elements form a natural base for the development
of a theory of the coevolution of genes and culture. In order
to increase the clarity of the unit, we matched it to the statistical definition of the 'artifact type' commonly used in
archaeology. The archaeologist, when presented with a
mixed collection of swords or other relics, takes numerous
measurements of their proportions, then compares the general appearance of all the specimens by a special statistical
technique called multiple dimensional scaling. Those specimens close enough to each other to form a tight cluster are
said to belong to the same artifact type. We decided to call
the basic unit the *culturgen* (from the Latin *cultura*, culture,
and *geno*, create) and to define it as a relatively homoge-
neous group of mental constructions or their products. In
our classification the manufacture or use of a particular
artifact type is therefore a culturgen. The same statistical
procedure can be used to group other kinds of behavior and
mental processes into culturgens. Psychological tests also
exist that allow the comparison of these clusters with node-
link structures in long-term memory. Overall, the culturgen
can be used as a concept in both psychology and the social
sciences.

Promethean Fire, pp. 120ff.

6

Culturgens and Memes

Culturgens are roughly what Dawkins has called 'memes' (see further pp. 69ff) — 'roughly', because Wilson and Lumsden are more formal in trying to model the probabilities of culturgen choice. A culturgen or meme does not have to be 'the smallest recognizable piece of cultural information' (J. A. Ball, 'Memes as replicators', *Ethology and Sociobiology*, V, 1984, p. 145). It can be a complex of artifacts, actions, or ideas, transmitted as a unit. In fact, turned inside out, a culturgen or meme is an item in the domain of culture (no matter what its size or complexity) that is variable and can be differentially transmitted. W. H. Durham has gone further and has proposed that the entire cultural repertory of variation for a given meme (after review, he has preferred the term 'meme'), whether they are actually chosen or not, should be called a 'holomeme'; and that the subset of holomemes that are, in fact, adopted by at least some members of a population at some time, should be known as 'allomemes' (*Coevolution: Genes, culture and human diversity*, Stanford University Press, 1991, p. 189).

The parallel in this last term with the word 'allele' (p. 23) in genetics is deliberate, and it draws attention to the importance of choice in defining culture. Choice is constrained by the epigenetic rules, which create a bias towards some choices rather than others — the human mind is *not* 'a beautiful blank sheet of paper'. The observable cultural patterns which distinguish one population from another

53

are, in effect, the majority sum of individual selections over *all* culturgens or memes. In strong theories of gene-culture coevolution, it is genetic selection which shapes the bias curves of choices, and it is for this reason that the genes hold culture on a leash, because either the survival of genetic information is enhanced or a particular cultural exploration will die out. Faced with a charging bull, what do you do? Run through all the available options to see which is the most appropriate, like making it a cup of tea or reciting to it alternate verses from 'The Ancient Mariner'? What is known in artificial intelligence research as 'the frame problem' means that unless all possible options and their consequences are narrowed down to the most strictly relevant, the optimal solution will never be found. The brain supplies the frame of most problems almost as soon as it recognizes a problem. It may not arrive at the *best* solution, but it arrives at *some* solution because it recognizes and supplies the frame of problem-solving. If a computer cannot supply the frame, the programmer must do so for it. Thus, in a frame-bounded problem, such as chess, the computer is highly effective. However, unless the computer knows the range of answers before, so to speak, it sees the problem, it will search for ever. Trial-and-error searches only work if the searcher — a brain or a computer — has a clear model of what is likely to be true of a domain, including a knowledge of what is erroneous.

Thus, what are known technically as 'domain-general, context-independent instructions' are useless in practice in guiding decisions. God, in the book of Leviticus, requires of Jews, 'Be holy as I am holy' (19.2), but, what, in practice, does 'being holy' involve? The highly detailed definition of 'practice' is precisely what fills Mishnah and Talmud, so much so that the prolific laws on keeping the sabbath day holy came to be described as 'a mountain hanging from a hair'. Christians may then dismiss (abusively, and without bothering about historical accuracy) such detailed explication as 'Pharisaic legalism', but they are not helped any more in practice by the attempt of Jesus to summarize the law and the prophets under two heads — the love of God and the love of one's neighbour. What *in practice* does it *mean* to love God and to love one's neighbour? The New Testament is already moving in the direction of greater detail, though still not enough to prevent schismatic conflict within the system as groups or individuals differ on the translation of domain-general, context-independent commands into domain-specific, context-dependent guidance (the implications of this are more fully discussed in Part III).

Returning, then, to computers and evolution: the 'frame problem' means that a computer must be supplied with the equivalent of 'innate knowledge' if it is to make any progress in an algorithmic search procedure, that is, one based on trial and error. If all options are genuinely options, even the most powerful computer simply cannot work through all the near-infinite possibilities. According to Strong Theories of gene-culture coevolution, the genetic 'search' for the optimum vehicle for the replication of its own code must, similarly, produce, in the case of the brain, innate knowledge of specific domains: thus incest avoidance, phobias, colour recognition and its coding cannot be learned afresh each time in each generation. Once again, the human mind is not a beautiful blank sheet of paper. What we may call 'Darwinian algorithms' require innate and developmentally invariant learning structures and recognition structures in the brain which can be expressed and reinforced in culture, where frames receive public and articulate form. The innate and invariant 'frame-builders' in the brain may then be activated by input from the internal or external environment, and will create an immediate bias in favour of domain-specific and domain-appropriate evaluations, judgements, and choices.

In this way, the genetic endowment in the human brain has equipped humans to make rapid discriminations of relevance which are crucial to survival. According to Strong Theories of gene-culture coevolution, this is to be traced to the epigenetic bias built into the human brain.

On this basis, the argument of Wilson and Lumsden can be represented as a reinforcing, homeostatic loop, taking colour discrimination as an example:

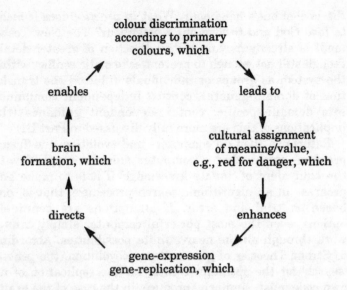

In this diagram, the genes build structures in the brain which build the specific and universal form of human colour recognition; this creates cultural opportunity, in the sense that the colour 'red' is so sufficiently differentiated by all people (except for those who are colour blind) from 'green' that 'red' can mean 'stop' and 'green' can mean go. There is no genetic *determinism,* since cultures can exploit genetic opportunity into differing outcomes: in some cultures, black is for mourning and white is for celebration, in others white is for mourning and black is for everyday wear. The homeostatic loop is formed if the chosen cultural decision enhances the probability of the genes being replicated which build the brain with that competence.

It does not, of course, follow that individuals have a free choice of memes or culturgens (cultural items) during their lives. Most choices have been made for them by their ancestors, and, indeed, the definition of culture in this sense is that it is the inherited set of culturgens into which people are born and in which people live. It is precisely because the chosen culturgens, dictated as they are by the epigenetic rules, have 'worked' that cultures endure through time, constraining human behaviour in very determinative ways.

For Strong Theories of gene-culture coevolution, the interaction between genes and culture means that gene frequencies are always, in the end, the controlling consideration. For Wilson and Lumsden, coevolution means 'any change in gene-frequencies that alters culturgen frequencies in such a way that culturgen changes alter gene-frequencies as well' (*Genes, Mind and Culture*, p. 372). This rules out the possibility that cultural achievements might gain an independent value and, therefore, a survival fitness, on their own account (i.e., independently of gene-replication). They therefore contrast their view with the conventional picture:

> The conventional picture of human evolution is one in which culture *replaced* genetic evolution: the brain evolved to a high level of capacity in memory and reasoning, all of a relatively generalized form, whereupon culture took over and guided mankind the rest of the way. According to this view, the past 25,000 years of history has consisted of dead reckoning with hereditary equipment acquired in earlier ages. But the evidence from cognitive psychology and the models of gene-culture coevolution point to a radically different relation between genes and mind. Although new forms of behavior, the 'mutations' of culture, are invented by the mind, which forms of innovation occur is very much influenced by the genes. A feedback then occurs from culture to the genes. The greater biological success of certain kinds of behavior causes the underlying epigenetic rules and their prescribing genes to spread through the population. Genetic evolution proceeds in this manner, rendering future generations more likely to develop the particular forms of thought and behavior that imparted success during the earlier tests by natural selection.
>
> Gene-culture coevolution is a radical process. The differences among individuals made possible by higher intelligence and culture enormously increase the potential for natural selection and genetic evolution. No longer do the genes dictate one or a very few behaviors—instead the mind intervenes decisively. Ranging widely, it creates a much greater array of actions. It permits each combination of genes to

have multiple expressions and offers alternative solutions to most problems within a single lifetime. Because the mind judges the circumstances of the moment and reflects on the broader implications of its own decisions, it can address the ordinary contingencies of life with greater moment-to-moment competence than the tightly programed responses of animals. In effect, the mutation rate of behavioral responses is vastly increased, and the genes that capacitated the responses are tested more rapidly than in ordinary, instinct-guided species.

As a result, evolution is accelerated. The genes continue to hold culture on a leash; in each generation the prevailing epigenetic rules of mental development affect which cultural innovations will be invented and which will be adopted. Yet culture is not just a passive entity. It is a force so powerful in its own right that it drags the genes along. Working as a rapid mutator, it throws new variations into the teeth of natural selection and changes the epigenetic rules across generations.

Promethean Fire, pp. 153ff.

7

Religions and Epigenetic Rules

In this perspective, the role of religion is obvious. As indicated earlier (pp. 37ff), religions are systems organized to protect and transmit those culturgens/memes which have served a selected purpose in enhancing the probability of gene-replication and the nurture of children. The beliefs, the hierarchies of decision and control, the priorities of boundary maintenance, the myths, rituals and symbols may differ greatly from one religion to another, but the function of religions — to protect and transmit information tested for effectiveness by natural selection — remains constant. Thus, in terms of belief, the cultural variations may be radically incompatible with each other. So, a human being may be constituted by an indestructible self (*atman*) being reborn in millions of lives (Hinduism), *or* the human being may be constituted by a coherent aggregation of energy in which there is no indestructible self to be found (*anatta* in Buddhism); the ultimate outcome for human beings may be a beautiful garden (alJanna in Islam), *or* it may be an impersonal state resembling thermodynamic equilibrium (nirvana in Buddhism); it may be union with Sri Krishna (Vaishnava Hinduism), *or* it may be absorption in Brahman as the unproduced source of all appearance (Advaita Hinduism); the cosmos may come into being as a consequence of the fiat of God (Judaism), *or* it may have no beginning and no end (Buddhism); the guide to faith and morals may be Scripture alone (Protestant

Christianity), *or* a single figure may be able to define some
such matters infallibly (Roman Catholic Christianity).

The list of examples could be extended almost indefinitely.
From the point of view of Sociobiology Mark I, the conflicts
are not simply insoluble, they are irrelevant. It does not
matter which particular beliefs sustain, by way of ideation,
any particular system, provided they serve the 'purpose' of
the genes. But in Sociobiology Mark II, religions at least
serve the additional purpose of being the most complicated
cultural constructions so far, elaborated from the epigenetic
rules. This means that they have been working effectively
as rapid mutators, throwing up a wide range of gene-based
options, to be tested and sifted in the usual ways by natural
selection. Each religion has then settled on a set of selected
options, elaborating impressive systems for ensuring wide
degrees of conformity, with the result that enduring religious traditions, whether at village or world level, are
inevitably conservative. Already one begins to see why
religions are involved in almost all the most intransigent
conflicts in the world: even without reference to content, it
is obvious that religions have been tested through millennia, and that they have worked. From the point of view of
Sociobiology Mark II, they have not led the gene-based
organisms to extinction, which means, in effect, that they
have been highly adaptive.

However, religions are now (according to sociobiologists)
massively maladaptive. Far from offering rapid mutation,
they are conservatively frozen in time. They endorse beliefs
that are irreconcilable with other knowledge, and behaviours that lead to conflict and ethical disaster. From the
point of view of an inhabitant of the science-based, technological societies of the twentieth century, it seems clear (at
least to sociobiologists) that what the mutually exclusive
beliefs of religions have in common is that most of them
(perhaps all of them) are false. That is why Wilson can
continue to make the claim that theology is finished, but
that religions will persist for some time yet (because of
their well-winnowed success through millennia in protecting the genes). What is required, in his view, is a better

'religion', and a wiser ethical system for the twenty-first century, which will track the genes more consciously and deliberately.

The immediate error in this analysis lies in the fact that it allows no room for genuine discoveries, abstracted from any considerations of gene fitness, in the cultural (in this case, the religious) systems. What is missing is any space for the possibility that the human brain (even allowing that it is 'gene-built') might make genuine recognitions of what is truly the case about its own nature and about the environments in which it is set. A brain, after all, can recognize a gene; it can also recognize beauty, truth, and goodness. These recognitions may have no adaptive advantages at all. Reverting to the earlier language of operational and cognized environments (Eo and Ec), the fact that the human mind mediates the construction of culture and religion does not mean, *ipso facto*, that the Eo cannot make independent demands which appear in the Ec, which are then carried in culture because of their own value, not simply because the *only* value is their contribution to the survival fitness of the relevant genes.

In that case, the recognition of God may be as well-founded and independent as the recognition of the universe or particular parts of it (although, obviously, God, if at all, is not an object among objects in the universe, so the procedures of recognition are not at all the same in both cases). Sociobiology has asked the question, 'Why should it have been *religious* systems that worked so well?', but, because it knows that the answer must relate content to gene-survival, the answers given turn out (as we shall see shortly) to be absurdly naive. What Sociobiology must necessarily exclude is the possibility that humans made specific discoveries about their internal and external environments which evoked the beliefs and actions that we call 'religious', including the discovery of God. While these may have been adaptive, it does not follow that all of those which have endured must have been so. In any case, even on the terms of Wilson's own argument, it is entirely possible that the discovery of God was as adaptive as other long-running cultural discoveries, and that, consequently, there is an epigenetic bias in favour of God, and, ultimately, of theology. In a far more careful and reflective way, the biogenetic structuralism of E. G. d'Aquili (see, e.g., *Biogenetic Structuralism*, 1974, *The Spectrum of Ritual*, 1979, *Brain, Symbol and Experience*, 1990) has argued that humans are prepared in the brain for many behaviours, including 'God'-recognizing behaviours.

The inverted commas in the last sentence round 'God' are simply a reminder that the languages through which these discoveries have been articulated belong to particular contexts. To repeat the point, all descriptive languages, including those of the natural sciences, and certainly those of theology, are approximate, provisional, corrigible, and, frequently, wrong, at least from the point of view of later generations. Yet, they achieve impressive reliability. This is because there is sufficient invariance in the operational environment for the cognized environment to attain degrees of descriptive correspondence or analogical claim (it is often overlooked that the very language of 'natural selection' selecting is analogical (see O. Mayo, *Natural Selection and its Constraints*, London, Academic Press, 1983, p. 2); and Sociobiology is clearly right to insist that there is sufficient invariance in the structures and substances of the brain for shareable and corrigible cognition to occur. In this interaction between the cognized and the operational environment, genuine discoveries occur in the natural sciences, even though there will never be an exhaustively complete description of 'what the universe is'.

The same is true, *mutatis mutandis*, of religious and theological exploration as well, as I argued at length in *Licensed Insanities*. To take one particular example, no one knows exactly 'what God is', and all theistic religions have come to insist emphatically on the point, but the experience of interaction with that which has evoked the language of *theos*, *deus*, Vishnu, Elohim, Allah, God, has, nonetheless, been sufficiently consistent and accessible for some (approximate) language to be required. The reference and meaning of this language, along with the actions, rituals, and symbols which sustain it, have been corrected and winnowed through time. But this process has not been controlled by 'survival fitness' with reference to the genes alone: there has been a survival fitness with reference to its *own* subject matter — in other words, with reference to the accessible truth of what the language purports to be about. If this were not so, it would be impossible to account for the massive changes and corrections in religious belief and practice that have occurred, despite the fact that religious systems are inherently conservative.

The failure to recognize this reduces Sociobiology as Wilson understands it to a grotesquely inadequate account of God-related behaviour. In *On Human Nature*, Wilson attempted to account for the behaviour of Mother Teresa in abandoning the pursuit of her own gene-replication behaviours in order to care for the poor and the dying in India. The fundamental reason, according to him, lies in reciprocal altruism (see p. 33) which has been distorted or (to use his own word) 'ossified' by religious imperialism:

> In sobering reflection, let us recall the words of Mark's Jesus: 'Go forth to every part of the world, and proclaim the Good News to the whole creation. Those who believe it and receive baptism will find salvation; those who do not believe will be condemned.' There lies the fountainhead of religious altruism . . . . Mother Theresa is an extraordinary person but it should not be forgotten that she is secure in the service of Christ and the knowledge of her Church's immortality.
>
> p. 165.

As an account of religious motivation, this may be able to be exemplified, but as an exhaustive account, it is ludicrous — not least because it cannot allow the possibility that religious security might be well-grounded. It is this possibility which creates the independence of culture and demands a weaker theory of gene-culture coevolution.

8

Weak Theories of Gene-Culture Coevolution: Short and Long Leashes

The contrast between strong and weak theories is clear. In the former, culture can always be mapped back onto the genes: it cannot be an autonomous process, creating the shareable diversity of human enterprise. But Weak Theories raise precisely this question: *is* culture so tied to the genes that it cannot declare a far greater degree of independence? *Total* independence is rejected by Wilson and Lumsden as 'the Promethean gene hypothesis'. This is the view that the genes build an organism which, like Prometheus, escapes from its earth — or gene-based — origin to capture fire from the gods — or, in the case of genes, to build a nature that has no nature (as Simone de Beauvoir put it). This would be so unstable (with all options to be tested in each generation) that evolution would be impossible.

Weak Theories take the point and have no ambition to divorce culture from genes altogether. Rather, they raise the question of whether or not the leash is so long that culture is free in many respects to pursue its own pathway, often in *opposition* to the interests of the genes. Take the example of dance. Bees engage in behaviours that humans, making an analogy from their own behaviours, describe as 'dance'. It is easy to see the rewards in terms of survival fitness of these 'cultural' behaviours, from the gene's point of view. In the case of bees, these behaviours are a way of communicating information vital for survival — for example, the direction in which they need to fly to find a site offering food or water; measures correlating with the distance (if the source is sufficiently distant: the information communicated in this respect is not so much the length of the journey as the intensity of it in terms of energy expenditure); and the value of the source (for a summary, see W. John Smith, *The Behaviour of Communicating: An ethological approach*, Cambridge, Harvard University Press, 1980, especially Chapter 6).

Extending this example, it is clear that the evolutionary rewards for the expenditure of energy on dance behaviours (making sexual displays, defining hierarchies, marking territory, etc.) can easily be mapped onto human behaviours. If genes hold culture on a *short* leash, then it is the 'selfish gene' which, ultimately, accounts for these dance behaviours, no matter how diverse they have become.

But now, in contrast, go to Covent Garden and watch the highly enculturated forms of Western ballet: what have these to do with gene-replication and the nurture of children? Certainly, the constituent parts of ballet are transmissible and heritable, undergoing change, and, thus, in a loose sense, ballet can be said to evolve; and 'ballet', either as a whole or in each of its parts, might be called a culturgen or meme. However, if culture is held on a *long* leash from the genes, one would expect to be able to trace the lineage of ballet from gene-protection behaviours, but one would also expect the human experience of dance to lead to developments which have taken on a cultural history of their own, depending particularly on the human capacity to discern *value* — in this case, the appreciation of beauty in music and movement — one part of the triad of values, namely, beauty, truth, and goodness.

Thus, when Kenneth MacMillan went to visit Benjamin Britten a week before he died, in order to get the story-line of *The Prince of the Pagodas* changed and strengthened, he was not held on a short leash from the genes: their decisions

did not link back to a survival value for gene-replication
and the nurture of children. It is true that all of MacMillan's
work was concerned, not simply with creating beauty, but
with illuminating the tragedies and the triumphs of human
interactions — not least those rooted in sexuality. As he
put it himself:

> I am very interested in people, and the dilemma of people
> living and working and being with each other: I wanted to
> draw that kind of thing into ballet. At that time, in the
> early 50s, that was not a very popular thing to do. People in
> choreography were interested in the purely decorative side,
> and I was not.
>
> 'Out of Line: a Portrait of Sir Kenneth MacMillan',
BBC TV, 1990.

This is very far from the kind of ethological behaviour
which can be so readily studied in other animal societies. If
ballet *is* held on a leash from the genes, the leash is so
long that the evolution of ballet has become sufficiently
detached to be governed by its own rules. W. John Smith
has made the point with precision, concluding his essay
on 'Ritual and the Ethology of Communicating' (in E. G.
d'Aquili (ed.), *et al.*, *The Spectrum of Ritual: A biogenetic
structural analysis*, New York, Colombia University Press,
1979):

> This proposal that human ritual is not a fundamentally
> new class of communicative behavior peculiar to our species
> does not imply that it has no human peculiarities . . .. The
> enormous cultural elaboration of our rituals correlates with
> their extension into peculiarly human enterprises such as
> worship and government. Human beings have reflected
> upon rituals, their causes, and their uses and have modified
> them to adjust their functioning. It would be fallacious to
> assume that human rituals are nothing more than elabor-
> ate versions of nonhuman ones, simply because a common
> origin is claimed. Human social behavior, managed with the
> highly specialized tool of language, is much more intricate
> than that of any other species. From studying biological
> origins and from comparing diverse species, we can gain

insights into the properties of such classes of behavior as displays and formalized interactions. But to discover what human beings can do with such classes and how human activities are constrained by them, we must study human behavior.

p. 76.

Weak Theories and the analogy between genetic and cultural evolution

Long-leash (i.e., weak) theories postulate (though the model is, in fact, as we shall see, defective) two parallel information systems, linked through the central nervous system and interacting in the formation of human behaviour and nature. Some then argue that it is feasible to use our present understanding of genetic evolution as an *analogy* for the history, process and diversity of human culture. For the sake of brevity, a weak theory making use of the analogy between genetic and cultural evolution will be called 'Weak Theory A'.

On this view, the units of cultural choice are regarded as being embedded in a separate information system which happens to be transmitted mainly through brains (still regarded, very often, as gene-built computers). It can still be accepted that there is a spin-off advantage to the genes that constrain the development of brains which choose cultural items or lifestyles that enhance the survival of the organism long enough for genes to be replicated; or, as Cloak put it more simply, 'a cultural instruction whose behaviour helps its human carrier-enactor (or his/her relatives) to acquire more children thereby has more little heads to get copied into' (F. T. Cloak, comment on E. E. Ruyle, *et al.*, 'The adaptive significance of cultural behaviour', *Human Ecology*, V, 1977, p. 50). Weak Theories, though, emphasize that cultural evolution has a history and process of its own: the issue for the 'analogy version' of a weak theory is to know to what extent cultural evolution 'mimics' genetic evolution so that the insights gained in the latter can be used to illuminate the former.

Thus, the key to any weak theory is that two information systems (the genetic and the cultural), which feed into phenotypic outcomes, are separate but interacting. While cultural choices *may* be rewarded in the genetic system (by affecting gene-frequencies and enhancing the probabilities of particular gene-replication), they do not *have* to be: culture evolves according to its own criteria of fitness and survival. The issue that differentiates Weak Theory A is that of knowing how closely the replication of cultural information resembles the replication of genetic information.

An example of Weak Theory A (a theory of coevolution based on analogy) is that of Dawkins — for example, in *The Selfish Gene* (Oxford University Press, 1976, 1989) and *The Extended Phenotype* (Oxford, W. H. Freeman, 1982). So far as analogy is concerned, he stated explicitly, 'Cultural transmission is analogous to genetic transmission in that, although basically conservative, it can give rise to a form of evolution' (*The Selfish Gene*, p. 188); and (on p. 190) he recognized that the analogy between cultural and genetic information has frequently been pointed out, but that he intends to go further. To do this, he believes that it is necessary to separate the evolutionary process of culture from that of the genes. Common to both is 'one fundamental principle: this is the law that all life evolves by the differential survival of replicating entities' (p. 92).

However, Dawkins is dissatisfied (to use his own word) with strong theorists who have assumed that there is only one kind of replicator (DNA), and who have, therefore, had to tie culture to the only replicator there is — who have been compelled, that is, 'to look for "biological advantages" in various attributes of human civilization' (p. 191). He commented:

> These ideas are plausible as far as they go, but I find that they do not begin to square up to the formidable challenge of explaining culture, cultural evolution, and the immense differences between human cultures around the world, from the utter selfishness of the Ik of Uganda, as described by Colin Turnbull, to the gentle altruism of Margaret Mead's Arapesh. I think we have got to start again and go right

back to first principles. The argument I shall advance, surprising as it may seem coming from the author of the earlier chapters, is that, for an understanding of the evolution of modern man, we must begin by throwing out the gene as the sole basis of our ideas on evolution. I am an enthusiastic Darwinian, but I think Darwinism is too big a theory to be confined to the narrow context of the gene. The gene will enter my thesis as an analogy, nothing more.

On the basis of this analogy, Dawkins proposed the name 'meme' for 'the new replicator' (p. 192), which is 'still in its infancy, still drifting clumsily about in its primeval soup, but already . . . is achieving evolutionary change at a rate that leaves the old gene panting far behind' (p. 192).

As examples of memes, he offered 'tunes, ideas, catchphrases, clothes fashions, ways of making pots or of building arches' (p. 192). On the analogy of co-adapted gene complexes (where a large set of genes may be so closely linked together in producing some phenotypical consequence that they can be regarded as a single gene — Dawkins gave as an example the genes involved in mimicry in butterflies), Dawkins recognized that a meme is not necessarily a single, discrete item. 'Democracy', for example, is an idea with many practical and theoretical realizations, in which many cultural items are brought together and linked. In order to be able to identify such meme complexes, Dawkins proposed a version of 'essentialism': we need simply to be able to pick out what *essentially* belongs to a proposed meme in order to be able to follow its fortunes. Thus, he argued:

> Similarly, when we say that all biologists nowadays believe in Darwin's theory, we do not mean that every biologist has, graven in his brain, an identical copy of the exact words of Charles Darwin himself. Each individual has his own way of interpreting Darwin's ideas. He probably learned them not from Darwin's own writings, but from more recent authors. Much of what Darwin said is, in detail, wrong. Darwin if he read this book would scarcely recognize his own original theory in it, though I hope he would like the way I put it. Yet, in spite of all this, there is something,

some essence of Darwinism, which is present in the head of every individual who understands the theory. If this were not so, then almost any statement about two people agreeing with each other would be meaningless. An 'idea-meme' might be defined as an entity that is capable of being transmitted from one brain to another. The meme of Darwin's theory is therefore that essential basis of the idea which is held in common by all brains that understand the theory. The *differences* in the ways that people represent the theory are then, by definition, not part of the meme. If Darwin's theory can be subdivided into components, such that some people believe component *A* but not component *B*, while others believe *B* but not *A*, then *A* and *B* should be regarded as separate memes. If almost everybody who believes in *A* also believes in *B* — if the memes are closely 'linked' to use the genetic term — then it is convenient to lump them together as one meme.

pp. 195ff.

Essentialism of the kind on which Dawkins relies requires far greater rigour than he affords it. To describe something as 'having an essence' is to maintain that it has essentially or necessarily certain properties without which it could not exist or be the thing that it is. Although essentialism of this kind goes back to Aristotle, it became connected in the twentieth century with discussions of *de dicto* and *de re* modalities. The enterprise of searching 'all brains that understand the theory' in order to identify the necessary properties without which the theory could not exist, so that we can then call this essence 'the meme of Darwin's theory', is clearly ludicrous, quite apart from which it is impracticable. The process of winnowing ideas and the transformation of them is indeed a part of what makes them interesting, but it is precisely because we talk of derivations from Darwin's initiative in terms of neo-Darwinian orthodoxy (from which, in any case, we have moved on) that 'brains which understand the theory' do not separate an essence of Darwinism from subsequent accretions or corrections. The accretions and corrections cannot be divorced from what we take 'Darwin's' theory to be, although, as historians, we may legitimately be interested in Darwin's *original* ideas. There is no nugget of Darwinism that passes through time disconnected from what has been made of his initiative since. Cultural ideas are woven of many strands, they are not discrete items, the essence of which can be identified and then isolated as memes that pass through brains apparently unaffected by the corrections and extensions of them.

If memes cannot be isolated and mapped via the route of essentialism, then the analogy with genes has become so remote that it is worthless (which is *not* to say that the study of cultural transmission cannot be done — clearly it can — but there are wiser and more sophisticated ways of undertaking it).

Gene sequences can, in fact, be mapped with great precision (otherwise the human genome project would be senseless) and genes can be identified which are involved in identifiable consequences (for example, cystic fibrosis or myotonic dystrophy, the identification of which has been claimed as an early result of the human genome project: see *Proceedings of the National Academy of Sciences*, LXXXIX, 1992, pp. 2231–5). To identify the essential nature of the democracy-meme, and then trace its consequence in the state of the British economy would be an impossible task. It is *not* impossible to make connections; though these will not resemble the formal and highly regular expression of genes in phenotypic consequences.

The analogy, as Dawkins handles it, is equally empty when one asks for the definition of cultural fitness. In the case of genes, a genotype can be defined, with Williams, as being 'fit' if its phenotypic characteristics are 'such as to make it likely to contribute a more than average number of genes to future generations: fitness may be defined as "effective design for reproductive survival"' (G. C. Williams, *Adaptation and Natural Selection*, New Jersey, Princeton, 1966, p. 158). What makes a meme 'fit' for reproduction and survival? Dawkins has emphasized, against Strong Theories of gene-culture coevolution, that '"survival value" does not mean value for a gene in a gene pool [because the information carried in memes is parallel to the information

carried in genes], but value for a meme in a meme pool'
(p. 193). So, the analogous question has to be, survival
value in relation to what? The analogous answer follows,
survival in relation to its own survival. What, though, gives
survival-value to memes? We are at once adrift on an uncharted ocean or, rather, not so much uncharted as 'charted
but ignored' by Dawkins, as historians and anthropologists
have given much thought to this question.

God as a virus

In contrast to the sophistication of their reflections, consider
the basis on which Dawkins argues that God is a virus. His
contention is that a God-meme can be identified (although
the absurdity of supposing that we could identify a common
essence in all the brains that understand 'the God theory'
is even greater in the case of God than it was in the case of
Darwinism, pp. 69–70). He allows that the God-meme may
have served some (dubious) purposes in the past, but now
those purposes cannot be served, because it has been
demonstrated that God is 'imaginary':

> The claim of the existence of God is a purely scientific one.
> Either it is true or it is not. A universe with God would be
> completely different from one without . . . . If you're deeply
> steeped in evolution, you see that it is a way to get complex
> designs out of nothing. You don't need God.
>
> *The Independent*, 16 April, 1992, p. 3.

The point is empty. As Gilbert Ryle pointed out in *Dilemmas*
(Cambridge University Press, 1954, pp. 94ff.), 'Ice could not
be thin if ice could not be thick'. If all examples are examples of the same thing, there is nothing to contrast them
with or, to put it the other way around, 'a country with no
coinage would offer no scope to counterfeiters: there would
be nothing for them to manufacture or pass counterfeits of'.
We cannot say (as opposed to imagine, as in science fiction)
what a universe other than this one would be like as we
only have the example of this universe; and this universe
will present itself evidentially in exactly the same way,

whether or not one thinks it more reasonable to suppose
that God is the unproduced Producer of it. If, to put it the
other way round, this is a universe *with* God, we cannot
say what a universe *without* God would be like — though,
given the inferential definition of God, we might well be
inclined to say that a universe without God could not exist,
and that a universe with God is what we see all around us.
Dawkins may be right to say that a universe without God
would be completely different (if, that is, it could exist at
all), but, logically, it is not a matter of scientific proof at all:
science can only explore the one universe that we happen
to have.

However, logic never interferes with Dawkins' arguments
where God is concerned. Having assumed that scientific
proof has shown that a universe with God would be different
from one without, and that science has not demonstrated
that this is a universe with God, he then proceeds to wonder why the God-meme continues to be transmitted from
brain to brain. He concludes that it is a parasite, and a
dangerous one at that, because it is a meme for which the
human race should have no further use (as it is false).
What, then, has given it its survival-value?

> Consider the idea of God. We do not know how it arose in
> the meme pool. Probably it originated many times by inde-
> pendent 'mutation'. In any case, it is very old indeed. How
> does it replicate itself? By the spoken and written word,
> aided by great music and great art. Why does it have such
> high survival value? Remember that 'survival value' here
> does not mean value for a gene in a gene pool, but value for
> a meme in a meme pool. The question really means: What is
> it about the idea of a god that gives it its stability and pene-
> trance in the cultural environment? The survival value of
> the god meme in the meme pool results from its great
> psychological appeal. It provides a superficially plausible
> answer to deep and troubling questions about existence. It
> suggests that injustices in this world may be rectified in the
> next. The 'everlasting arms' hold out a cushion against our
> own inadequacies which, like a doctor's placebo, is none the
> less effective for being imaginary. These are some of the

reasons why the idea of God is copied so readily by successive generations of individual brains. God exists, if only in
the form of a meme with high survival value, or infective
power, in the environment provided by human culture.

The Selfish Gene, pp. 192ff.

As an account of religious motivation, this has about as
much value as three feathers in a chicken shed. It is as far
removed from evidence and data as is Wilson's account of
Mother Teresa. The 'placebo theory' can surely be *exemplified*, though, in fact, it has to be remembered, as I have
shown in *The Meanings of Death* (Cambridge University
Press, 1991), that, in origin, the major religious traditions,
both East and West, had no belief in a worthwhile life after
death at all. Much else can be exemplified as well which
contradicts Dawkins' facile account. However, following
the line of Dawkins' argument, the continuingly 'infective
power' of a false meme means that it resembles the power
of parasites to ride on the back of other organisms. For
him, therefore, the best analogy is that of a virus. A virus is
a micro-organism made up of a protein, or protein/lipid
sheath, containing nucleic acid (either DNA or RNA). A
virus is inert outside living cells, but if it can get inside an
appropriate cell as a parasite, it then uses the cell to fuel
its own replication. These give rise to viral diseases like
chicken-pox or flu or, more seriously, to yellow fever or
AIDS.

Once again, the analogy is remote because the particular
parasite of the God-meme does not give rise to one set of
consequences — the equivalent of flu. Out of the many
behaviours it produces, why are we required to isolate only
those that might be regarded as diseased? And who, in any
case, decides, and on what grounds, what is diseased? It
becomes clear that there is nothing here as objective as the
observation of chicken-pox. The value (in the judgement of
survival-value) is that of the observer, which is itself a consequence of culture and so is highly relative. One might
share Dawkins' passionate hatred of religion or of God, and
one might find some warrants or reasons for such hatred.
What he says about the consequences of 'faith in God' can

surely be *exemplified* (though, once again, in terms of evidence, his account of what the God-meme 'does' for believers is descriptively false in the case of the earliest history of religions, as I have shown in *The Meanings of Death*). All this, though, is extremely distant from the objectivity with which one can observe symptoms, identify causes, and isolate 'malaria'. The fact that we are dealing, in Dawkins' case, with enculturated prejudice becomes even more obvious when we observe his handling of 'faith':

> Another member of the religious meme complex is called faith. It means blind trust, in the absence of evidence, even in the teeth of evidence. The story of Doubting Thomas is told, not so that we shall admire Thomas, but so that we can admire the other apostles in comparison. Thomas demanded evidence. Nothing is more lethal for certain kinds of meme than a tendency to look for evidence. The other apostles, whose faith was so strong that they did not need evidence, are held up to us as worthy of imitation. The meme for blind faith secures its own perpetuation by the simple unconscious expedient of discouraging rational inquiry.
>
> Blind faith can justify anything. If a man believes in a different god, or even if he uses a different ritual for worshipping the same god, blind faith can decree that he should die — on the cross, at the stake, skewered on a Crusader's sword, shot in a Beirut street, or blown up in a bar in Belfast. Memes for blind faith have their own ruthless ways of propagating themselves. This is true of patriotic and political as well as religious blind faith.
>
> *The Selfish Gene*, p. 198.

This, though, is to descend to a new depth of absurdity. Faith does not mean 'blind trust, in the absence of evidence, even in the teeth of evidence'. Like many other words, it does not 'mean' any one, simple thing. In human usage, one can have faith in many different things or people — in one's car, one's spouse, the word of politicians, the rising of the sun, the honesty of the scientists who discovered the genetic code, the consistency of chemical reactions, and, yes, God. Of course one's faith may be profoundly misplaced (and perhaps only others can, in some instances, perceive this). There is a necessary empiricism in all faith, including religious faith; or, again, one's faith in the consistency of chemical reactions may be a matter of blind trust (because, for example, one's education never called into question the foundations of science), but, if pressed, one could find (or attempt to find) warrants for such trust. In a comparable way, one may be initiated into faith in God in such a way (or in such communities) that it is, indeed, a matter in practice of blind faith. However, it does not follow that no warrants for this trust can be found (many examples are given in my earlier books, e.g., *The Sense of God: Sociological, Anthropological and Psychological Approaches to the Sense of God* (Oxford University Press, 1973; new edn., One World Press, 1995), *The Religious Imagination and the Sense of God* (Oxford University Press, 1978), *Licensed Insanities*, 1987). To assert otherwise is nothing but blind prejudice of a particularly arrogant kind.

It now becomes obvious that, where Dawkins is concerned, there is nothing objective in deciding what supplies survival fitness; it is a highly personal and prejudiced decision on his part. In his 1992 lecture, *Viruses of the Mind* (British Humanist Association, 1992), he attempted to distance science from the observation that it, too, as it is transmitted through human brains, is also a virus. Not so, he replied, because 'the selective forces that scrutinize scientific ideas are not arbitrary or capricious'. In contrast to faith, 'they favour all the virtues laid out in textbooks of standard methodology: testability, evidential support, precision, quantifiability, consistency, intersubjectivity, repeatability, universality, progressiveness, independence of cultural milieu, and so on' (p. 15). Yet this is simply to specify some conditions of epistemology and truth claims in the case of the natural sciences. These are not the only criteria of true or worthwhile human utterance. They do not all apply, for example, to art, music, sculpture, or poetry. His criteria rule out the possibility that truth can be told by a poet; though obviously, if the poet wins a Nobel Prize, it is going to be for literature, and not for science. Theology also has its own criteria for what counts as true or appropriate utterance. The point is that cultural achievements (i.e., what Dawkins calls 'memes') are related to the human judgements of truth, beauty, and goodness. Clearly, the genes contribute to the development of brains that are capable, in the human case, of making these judgements; and no matter how culturally relative many of these judgements may be (though less so in the case of truth, which makes Dawkins' refusal to consider evidence in the case of belief in God all the more bizarre), the human competence to make them, being conserved and transmitted in the human developmental system, is virtually universal.

Coevolution

It is the recognition of this independence of judgement that gives impetus to the more serious of the weak theories of gene-culture coevolution.

Of these, the most detailed is that of W. H. Durham (*Coevolution: Genes, culture and human diversity*, Stanford University Press, 1991). For him, the central question is, as with all other theories, 'What are the most important causes of transformation in cultural evolution? What, in other words, are the principle processes by which cultural systems change through time, and how do these processes relate to the dynamics of change in the corresponding genetic system of inheritance?' (p. 185). To these questions he gave the following answer:

I have proposed that genes and culture are best represented as two parallel lines or 'tracks' of hereditary influence on phenotypes . . . . In this proposal, culture's relationship to phenotypes is structurally symmetrical to that of the genes [i.e., information of both kinds has influence, actual or potential, over the observable phenotypic properties of human beings, particularly their behaviours]; it is truly a 'paragenetic' transmission system (after Waddington, 'The human evolutionary system', in M. Banton, ed., *Darwinism and the Study of Society*, University of Chicago Press, 1961, p. 72). The proposal builds on ideational theories of culture and their suggestion that culture provides socially trans-

mitted guides to behaviour. In my opinion, these arguments
are crucial if social science is to make significant headway
past the barriers of the nature/nurture debate.

p. 420.

Durham accepted from Dawkins the terminology of 'meme'
to represent the variable unit of transmission in cultural
evolution: a meme can be any kind, amount, or configura-
tion of information in culture that shows both variation
and coherent transmission. However, he emphasized that
the analogy with 'the gene' is imperfect: 'there are major
disanalogies, the most important of which concerns the
variability of the meme in scale and organization' (p. 422).
This distinction set him free from the distorting restrictions of the argument from analogy. In particular, it
allowed him to build into his analysis of cultural evolution
precisely what is excluded from genetic evolution, namely,
selection by *choice*, not simply selection by consequence, as
it is for the genes.

This brings us back, yet again, to the human discern-
ment of value. Clearly, many cultural outcomes are a result
of decisions or choices made that are based on evaluation.
On what basis are these evaluations made? In a pioneering
study, George Pugh offered a systems description of 'the
value-driven decision system' located in the human brain.
In any decision system, the designer (in this case the evolution of the human brain on the basis of adaptive variations
in development) can build in 'primary values'. These, on
Pugh's analysis, are 'valuative sensations which are experienced as *intrinsically* good or bad, pleasant or unpleasant'
(G. E. Pugh, *The Biological Origin of Human Values*, New
York, Basic Books, 1977, p. 112). These are not learned;
they are built into the reward system of the brain, and
create a bias in the direction of choice, even though they
might be culturally overridden by decisions derived from
the 'secondary value' system.

The secondary value system does not arise from ontogeny
or from individual experience, but from collective wisdom
and tradition. These may be enshrined in law, convention,
proverbs, principles, and so on, and they are used to guide

or control decision-making. Pugh's own argument lends itself to Strong Theories of gene-culture coevolution, because he regarded the 'evolutionary design objective' of the human decision system to be 'survival of the species' (pp. 29–31). Durham can accept that there is, indeed, a biological base (in the way human brains are constructed) for the evaluative judgements that guide cultural choice. However, 'survival of the species' is not always the overriding constraint on this choice. Thus, Durham disentangled five distinct modes of relationship between genetic and cultural change in human populations. Two are interactive ('a change in one system, genetic or cultural, within a population, or a difference between the systems, genetic or cultural, of two populations, causes a change in the fitness values . . . . governing evolution in the other system', p. 436), but the other three he called 'comparative', *because there is no interdependent change*: 'Instead, culture evolves through self-selection in directions that may or may not be consistent with maximum Fg [i.e., reproductive fitness, measurable at the microlevel by inclusive fitness-value].' This allows for cultural developments that may be in opposition to anything that 'the selfish gene' would have designed for itself (in fact, of course, the selfish gene cannot 'design' anything, whereas humans, in the case of culture, can).

9

Genes and Their Environment

Even so brief a description of Durham's proposals makes it clear that it is entirely possible to put forward a theory of gene-culture coevolution which pays more attention to the way in which genes are embedded in a developmental process: they are as much dependent on other parts of the process as they are necessary to it. Genes cannot be isolated from the process as though they are the controlling agents, organizing and directing the whole enterprise for their own (selfish) purpose. Development depends not simply on what has been inherited from parents (genes and other materials in sperm and egg), but on cell activity, cell division, ambience, nutrition, and, eventually, sensory inputs that the developing organism experiences. For example, it is now well known that the environment inside the womb is vital in controlling fetal weight — it is not simply a matter of gene-programmes being unfolded. Thus, different organs mature at different times, during periods of rapid cell division, before birth and during infancy (e.g., the pancreas continues to develop after birth, the kidneys develop during the last three months of pregnancy). The time of rapid cell division is known as 'the sensitive period'. While the initiation of this may, in part, be under genetic control, the unfolding of the process is not. Interference with the fetus or infant (e.g., through malnutrition) during the sensitive periods has permanent effects — so much so that the phenomenon has been called (ironically) 'programming'; these consequences are clearly *not* a result of genetic programmes. A well-known example of this other kind of programming is the effect of injecting female rats with a single injection of the male sex hormone, testosterone, on the fifth day after birth. The result is that they never ovulate, and they fail to exhibit other marks of female sexual behaviour. If they are injected only a day or two later, it does not have the same marked effect. At the moment, it is not known in what ways many of these 'programming' effects work, but, in general, it is clear that a change is effected in transiently susceptible cell populations permanently affecting the sequence of reciprocally selective interactions between genes and developmental conditions. In this case, it is clearly wrong to regard the genes as agents of cellular change, but, rather, as constrained and constraining components of an altered and alterable developmental system.

Even at the simplest and most elementary levels, it becomes obvious that the gene cannot be isolated from the entire activity of the cell, and that the evocation or suppression of gene-transcription or gene-expression depends on the many environments in which cellular activity is set. Thus, the cleaner fish, *Labroides dimidiatus*, is a territorial fish, with the male owner of a territory controlling a harem of five or six females. The male is the largest fish, but the females also form a size-based hierarchy. When the male dies, the largest, dominant female takes over the territory and, within hours, is controlling the harem. Within two weeks, the now male fish is producing sperm.

It becomes obvious, also, that one cannot give priority to the genes in isolation as the controlling agents in the building of bodies and beyond bodies of culture. Nor do they contain codes, or programmes, or information that dictate the building of bodies as survival machines. It makes sense to say that the primary structure of a polypeptide is encoded on the chromosomes; such polypeptide chains generally have only a few thermodynamically stable three-dimensional configurations, so that, in most circumstances, the genetically encoded linear structure determines the three-dimensional structure. This, though, is a very long way from saying that information is encoded in the genes which build the proteins which build the body as a gene-survival machine. In fact, even if the entire molecular specification of every gene in an organism were known, it would not be possible to predict what the organism would be.

None of this is to deny the importance of what the genes do. If we speak 'of mice and men', the differences between them are almost entirely a consequence of the differences in the genes between them. To take a more restricted example, no one can be unaware of the connection between pathological conditions and genetic causes. In some cases, such as cystic fibrosis and Huntington's Chorea, these are unitary genetic causes. Nevertheless, even here, there is no working out of an inevitable genetic programme, as though modification of the environment can never make a difference. To take a well-known example, PKU (phenylketonuria) is an inherited autosomal recessive error of metabolism in which the enzyme phenylalanine hydroxlase is defective. Whereas this enzyme ordinarily catalyses the conversion of the amino acid phenylalanine to tyrosine, when the enzyme is defective the conversion is critically slowed, with elevated plasma phenylalanine resulting. In childhood, these elevated levels have a toxic effect on neuron mylenization, which leads to gross cognitive impairment, fits, and microcephaly. However, a screening test for the condition in new-born infants exists which allows homozygous recessive individuals to be identified and placed on restricted phenylalanine diets, thus preventing the elevated levels from occurring. It is now possible for 75 per cent of such homozygous recessives to attend normal schools. A similar example of the way in which the consequences of a defective gene are not inevitable, but can be altered by attending to the developmental environment, is Wilson's disease. This, again, is an autosomal recessive defect which causes excessive intestinal absorption of the copper that is consumed (in minute amounts) by everyone in his or her food. As the copper accumulates in the body, it causes nervous degeneration and, eventually, premature death. However, the lifetime taking of pyridoxine and D-penicillamine mobilizes copper from the tissues and promotes its excretion in the urine. The consequences of the genetic contribution to life-history, far from being deterministic, have been completely changed by alterations in the environment.

Causes and constraints

It becomes clear, therefore, that the fundamental error of many theories of gene-culture coevolution is that they over-simplify the ways in which genes and culture cause or produce phenotypical outcomes. They assume two systems of information, the genetic and the cultural, which shape these outcomes, and they then try to determine which of the two is dominant in producing particular outcomes. As no one maintains that phenotypical outcomes are caused by *only* the one or the other, the endeavour becomes one of weighting the causative contribution of each in interaction with the other.

There are two obvious defects in this endeavour. The first is that the word 'information' raises false expectations. Technically (as in information theory), information can be analysed mathematically and statistically without reference to content at all, but colloquially, information implies content, so that a policeman informs you of your rights by telling you what they are; messages are left for arriving passengers at airports at information desks. The transmission of the genetic code (in the sense already established, pp. 28f.) can usefully be analysed in terms of entropy and redundancy (i.e., with insights derived from information theory), but it certainly cannot (or should not) be discussed as though it is passing on information in the colloquial sense (i.e., the genes are not packed with content-full messages that tell the organism what it is to do).

The second defect lies much deeper, in the way in which the notion of 'cause' is understood. The assumption is that there are two 'causes' — genes and culture — which are forcing the pliant organisms into shape and behaviour: they are the sergeant and the corporal on the parade ground, drilling the platoon. This is an almost inevitable

assumption in a post-Newtonian world, in which we model
the notion of 'cause' on a sense of 'active force'. Force is a
vector quantity, with both a magnitude and a direction; in
an interaction between objects, one exerts a force on another.
Despite the caution of Hume (that we never observe 'cause',
but only a constancy of conjunction from which we *infer*
'cause'), the consistency of action and reaction is such that
the sense of force remains dominant. Applied to the issue of
the 'cause' of human behaviours, the question inevitably
becomes, 'What is it that "forces" the plastic material of
human bodies into their characteristic outcomes? Is it the
selfish gene, which builds survival machines in order to
secure the replication of the genetic information? Or is it
culture, which builds a second skin within which the information is protected?' Note how, in both cases, the language
of agency creeps in. Of course, such language is always
qualified by an emphasis that 'the genes are not purposive',
that 'culture is the product, not the conscious producer', but
the point remains obvious: 'cause', as 'the force which
brings things about', leads inevitably to a selection of the
truly coercive and operative forces that have produced the
result in question. Backed up by a version of Ockham's
Razor ('where one explanation will do, don't multiply explanations'), we arrive at the situation in which we at present
find ourselves: human behaviour is caused by simple
forces, the genes in some combination with culture. It then
remains a question how to weigh (or quantify) the relative
contribution of each.

10

The Ontogeny of Information

The dangers in this pervasive oversimplification have been pointed out with great clarity by Susan Oyama in her book, *The Ontogeny of Information* (Cambridge University Press, 1985). In her view, the failure of current interactionist attempts to understand human nature — the 'what I am' of human beings — lies in the domain assumption of Western thought, that form and order are imposed by a pre-existing agent on chaos or on formless matter. It then makes no difference whether it is God, or Newtonian mechanisms, or evolution, or gene-programmes in the cell — the structure of argument is the same: a pre-existing source of plan and information imposes order on what would otherwise be randomness or chaos, which in this case is a random pile of chemicals. And because, in general, the human mind prefers simplicity, it tends to look for one single agent, possessed of the plan, who (or which) imposes the order. The truth of this can be seen in the way in which each stage eliminates or subordinates the necessity for the previous 'agent'. So, with Newtonian mechanics, you do not need God; with evolution, you need more than Newtonian mechanics; with gene-programmes, you need evolution only as a referee of success or failure.

In this context, the problem of culture in relation to genes becomes clear: the genetic code, or the information in the genes, is claimed to be the agent that forms (informs) human nature, but culture seems to be an agent 'forming'

human nature as well. In this domain assumption of force
and order, there is no way to handle the problem of 'what
imposes human order on otherwise random chemicals',
except to say that, in some manner, they both do, hence the
inevitability of interactionist language. Both genes *and* culture contain the information which dictates the outcome into
the phenotype. However, Oyama points out that the 'model'
of the finished or accomplished phenotype does not, as a
matter of fact, lie preformed in either the genes or in culture. Genes may contribute to muscle development via
proteins, and culture may include boxing boards of control
which govern the ways in which boxers' muscles may be
used in boxing, but they do not hold blueprints that dictate
what each phenotypical boxer is like in training, skill, or
style, nor even how he develops his muscles. All these
phenotypical consequences emerge in the developmental
process of a particular life-history, which is controlled into
its outcomes by many constraints, and not just by genes
imposing blueprints, instructions, or codes, even in conjunction with culture. Although, as she says, 'the genetic
code' has become part of everyday language, codes are
limited in what they can translate and translate into:

Though the genetic code has become part of everyday language, a brief discussion of this variant is necessary. It is
often combined with others, as in coded information or
instructions. It is clear that whatever problems arise with
these other versions are not solved by claiming that they
are encoded in the genes rather than literally being present
in them. A code does not alter the content of a message,
only its form. While it makes sense in general to say that
the primary structure of a polypeptide is encoded on the
chromosomes, and while such a string generally has only a
few thermodynamically stable, three-dimensional configurations (so that under most circumstances the linear structure determines the three-dimensional one), it is not clear
what else may be said to be thus encoded.

Gatlin describes a code as a way of mapping a domain
onto a counter-domain. If several elements in the domain
code for (map onto) the same element in the counterdomain,

a degenerate relation exists. This is the case in the genetic system, where several codons can code for the same amino acid. Ambiguity, on the other hand, exists when an element in a domain maps onto more than one element in the counterdomain. By her definitions, a relation that is both degenerate and ambiguous does not even seem to be a code . . . .

This formal requirement of a code should be kept in mind. When Lumsden and Wilson, for example, speak of 'compressible systems' which can be 'described or regenerated by a set of rules or instructions much shorter than the shortest direct description of the system itself,' and go on to say that it is possible 'to recover the original system in detail', . . . they seem to be speaking of some sort of mapping. But though they suggest that human social phenomena fit this model, their unilinear causal scheme (genes to epigenesis to individual behavior to culture. . . .) is not consistent with the degeneracy and ambiguity found in ontogenetic processes at many levels. In the phenocopy, several genotypes are associated with the same phenotype; this also occurs whenever there is genetic variability that is not reflected in phenotypic variability, that is to say, very frequently. Mapping ambiguity is observed whenever a genotype is associated with several phenotypes; this would include the differentiation of tissues during ontogenesis and the norm of reaction for a given genotype. The same argument can be made for any particular environmental variable or event. Many stimuli may be functionally equivalent for an organism, and a given stimulus may call out a variety of responses (or none) from an organism at different times or from different organisms. In ontogenetic processes, then, neither developmental interactants nor phenotypes are uniquely recoverable from each other. Where then is the code?

pp. 70ff.

Oyama's point then becomes obvious, that the phenotype is a consequence of a developmental process in which the activity of gene transcription and the context of cultural constraint play their part, but *not* in any standard or invariant or even exclusive way. How genes and culture contribute to any particular phenotype in the process of its

unfolding history depends on that particular history. One
may legitimately say that both genes and culture are necessary conditions of human nature, and are constant in the
network of constraint that controls all eventualities into
their outcome, into their being what they are. However,
they are not sufficient conditions to explain every phenotypical event, no matter how widely the term 'culture' is
spread. Still less can they explain human nature by the
belief that they somehow 'contain' the plan of human
nature, as the differentiating effects in development of *any*
developmental interactant — whether genetic or environmental — is determined in relation to the other developmental conditions and constraints present. They cannot be
assumed to unfold identically, irrespective of variation in
these other conditions and constraints. Human nature is
better understood as a consequence of a developmental
process in which the difference made by any given interactant (i.e., the difference which makes a difference) is multiply constrained, being a function of the history of the system
and its current state: hence the phrase, 'the ontogeny of
information'. Oyama therefore concluded:

> What we are moving toward is a conception of a develop-
> mental system, not as the reading off of a preexisting code,
> but as a complex of interacting influences, some inside the
> organism's skin, some external to it, and including its eco-
> logical niche in all its spatial and temporal aspects, *many of*
> *which are typically passed on in reproduction* either because
> they are in some way tied to the organism's (or its con-
> specifics') activities or characteristics or because they are
> stable features of the general environment. It is in this
> ontogenetic crucible that form appears and is transformed,
> not because it is immanent in some interactants and nour-
> ished by others, or because some interactants select from a
> range of forms present in others, but because any form is
> created by the precise activity of the system. Since even
> species-typical 'programmed' form is not one but a near-
> infinite series in transition throughout the life cycle, each
> whole and functional in its own way, to refer to the type or
> the typical is also to refer to this series and the constant
> change that generates it.

If the genome, highly structured and integrated as it is, cannot by itself explain the products of ontogenetic change (the cognitive, planning function), can it at least be seen as the driving force (the causal, volitional, energetic function) of such change? Much is written about the genes initiating, engendering and originating, and the idea of diminutive chemical engines powering biological processes is appealing. In fact, of course, a gene initiates a sequence of events only if one chooses to begin analysis at that point; it occupies no privileged energetic position outside the flux of physical interactions that constitutes the natural (and the artificial) world. A seed may remain dormant for years, and though plants frequently show this kind of developmental passivity, it is observed among animals as well . . .. Genes affect biological processes because they are reactive, and this reactivity is a prime characteristic of our world, at all levels of analysis, from the subatomic through the social to the astronomical. To describe biological processes as the product of exchanges of energy, matter and information, . . . while consistent with the temper of the times, is misleading in seeming to postulate a third, quasi-physical force at work in the world. Both the initiation and the course of biological change are a function of developmental systems, and there is no evidence that our notions of matter and energy exchanges, themselves admittedly evolving, are inadequate to describe them. Adding information to matter and energy is something like speaking of nations exchanging dollars, yen and profits. The third term belongs on a different level. Not another form of currency, it describes a certain disposition and use of currencies. Just as time or information can, under certain circumstances, 'be' money, matter and energy can sometimes 'be' information.

Oyama, therefore, argued that many developmental conditions and interactants, and not just genes, can be sources of variation and stability between and within organisms. Evolution does indeed proceed by the differential survival of replicating entities. What she has rejected is the 'selfish gene' perspective, which regards genes as taking advantage of any developmental opportunity in the network of conditions and interactions constituting the 'extended phenotype' to produce the variations on which selection operates. In place of Dawkins' gene-centred view, which sees 'causal networks as exploitation and one-way control', Oyama identified the ecologically embedded, interdependent and contingent developmental systems that constitute these networks as the units of selection (pp. 124 and 157).

The concept of the developmental system opens up analysis to include any heritable variation in developmental constituents and their interactions, not just genes, bearing in mind Oyama's crucial proviso that the developmental relevance of a given constraint is determined by the system in which it is embedded. This is in contrast to the conventional view that evolution occurs by differential gene transmission alone, with the role of ontogeny in evolution being only 'to land the organism in reproductive condition at the apex of its biological career' (p. 155).

In considering Oyama's view, the question arises of what kinds of non-genetic interactant can vary without grossly disturbing viable development *and* be transmitted so that selection can operate. Oyama's examples suggest that such interactants may be intracellular or be a reliably recurrent feature of the external environment consistently linked to ontogeny to eventuate in a selectable variation (Dawkins' 'extended phenotype' is similar, in so far as it can include other organisms, their genes, and relevant inorganic conditions).

In the case of intracellular interactants, major variation in the non-genetic constituents would seem to be precluded by the necessity for overall stability in conditions, especially given the scope for genetic novelty in parental meiosis: if variation is too great, then the sequences of reciprocally selective interactions producing development would unravel and the system would not be viable. Yet a minor change in a non-genetic constituent of the system could produce significant yet viable change in the phenotype, depending on the change, the cellular system in which it occurs, and the developmental surround.

Thus, Oyama cites Raff and Kaufmann's account of the sea urchin embryo (p. 129). Initially, this includes, first, the organism's genome, second, complex cell structures (e.g., the cytoskeletal matrix), and, third, mRNA, derived from the mother's genome, not the embryo's own. The second and third parts bring development of the sea urchin embryo to the blastula stage without any transcription of the organism's genes. Thus, phases of development within an organism occur without gene-expression, though everything present within the embryo, *ab initio,* has been constructed in the parent by processes and materials partly involving gene-expression. If an alteration in embryonic maternal mRNA produced a change in development, which resulted in an altered but viable phenotype, selection could, in principle, occur. While a change in mRNA may be attributable to genetic change in the mother, its developmental relevance for the embryo is a joint function of the change and the developmental system in which it occurs, which, for heritable variation to occur, must include any developmental conditions and constraints at any level of complexity that are reliably present or reassembled from one generation to the next. The importance of considering the developmental system as a whole is underlined when we consider how the sets of relationships constituting the system itself may be transformed by an altered phenotype, as the new phenotype may change the developmental relevance of constituents of the genome or environment — in the latter case, for example, sufficiency or type of nutrients, responsiveness to temperature, predator relationships, and so on.

Thus, the adaptive relevance of such sets of relationships are illustrated by Oyama with reference to the *Drosophila* fly, which must emerge from the puparium as an adult at dawn to avoid dessication: 'The adaptively significant variable is moisture, but it is not moisture but dark-light transition, which occurs just enough earlier to give the organism sufficient lead time, to which the insect's internal clock is synchronised' (p. 136). If dark-light transition occurred when humidity was low, the emerging adult would be dessicated and the developmental system would not be reproduced; its viability depends on a consistent relationship between environmental variables, enabling the entrainment of the internal clock of the insect to dark-light transition to be an adaptive feature of its developmental system. Thus light intensity is effectively part of the developmental system that is selected along with other developmental conditions and interactants in so far as it differentially constrains development in a consistent way from one generation to the next.

In a further example, Oyama argues that Waddington's genetic assimilation research showed that 'a creature developed in ways that depended on its circumstances, and that, far from being irrelevant to evolution, such ontogenetic variation could on occasion be crucial to it' (p. 150). Waddington exposed *Drosophila* pupae to intense heat, which produced a specific change in wing structure. After several generations of breeding from the flies that responded most strongly to the heat stimulus, the change in wing structure developed in the absence of the stimulus. Oyama interprets these results as showing that there are several ways of developing the character, each way genetically and environmentally contingent: '(1) the original genotype in the altered circumstances, (2) the selected genotype in the altered circumstances, and (3) the selected genotype in the original circumstances. One can, furthermore, sometimes move by selection from one way to another. This multiplicity of developmental possibilities gives the species grace time to adapt genetically to new conditions, at the same time giving selection a new process on which to work' (p. 150ff.).

In Oyama's view, then, genes are necessary but not sufficient in the explanation of ontogeny and phylogeny, including that of human beings. She suggested, therefore, a far more sophisticated research programme that would be sensitive to the complexity of what is going on:

> Pronouncing traits to be biological rather than cultural answers nothing, but investigation of the relations between physiological and psychological levels might reveal a great deal about how those systems work. If ontogeny is a matter of nested causal systems whose functional order is a result of the running of the system, not of any one set of its constituents, if phylogeny is progressive change in these

developmental systems, and if, furthermore, the course of phylogeny is influenced by what can and cannot happen in ontogeny, while ontogeny is constrained by many of the very functional requirements that shape the species' history, then understanding of either requires 'unpacking' the developmental system. Although a character may develop in any number of ways and still be adaptive, understanding how it evolved implies some knowledge of its development. Rather than being guided by some overarching strategy of identifying innate components or separating genetic and environmentally determined variance while considering gene-environment correlation and interaction an embarrassment (or simply excluding them from models), we might reasonably focus on the correlations and interactions themselves.

p. 159.

An example of this approach in practice is M. H. Johnson and J. Morton's, *Biology and Cognitive Development: The case of face recognition* (Oxford, Blackwell, 1991; cf. Wilson, p. 50). They suggest a framework for identifying the different levels of genetic and environmental organization and ways in which their interactions can be developmentally relevant. They define three levels at which environment and genotype can interact in development.

First, the environment within the genetic material; the location of a gene in the genetic material will determine when it is expressed, and with which other genes (in conjunction with other constraints); second, the local biochemical environment which can either act with gene products, or act upon the gene itself (in the phenylketonuria example, p. 82, abnormal neural development is produced by the interaction of a defective gene product with a biochemical environment containing phenylalanine derived from the diet); third, the interaction between the product of the first two levels (the internal environment) and the world outside the organism (the external environment).

The external environment is further divided into the *species-typical environment* (STE) and the *individual-specific environment* (ISE). They illustrate the distinction with an

example from ethology. Godfrey Gottlieb found that mallard ducklings show a preference for the mallard species'
call compared with other duck calls without previous exposure to mallard duck calls. This was then interpreted as
demonstrating an innate preference for the conspecific call
amongst mallard ducklings.

However, later research demonstrated that the conspecific
call preference only developed following exposure to the
'contact contentment call' made by the embryonic chick in
the day before hatching, which bears no resemblance to the
adult call (pp. 6f.): 'Since this particular input is common to
all normal members of the species, it would be charac-
terised as being part of the STE. Further learning about a
particular adult bird's call, an experience unique to an individual, would be part of the ISE' (p. 10).

A further distinction is drawn between *specific* and *non-
specific* information from the STE. In the case of the mallard
ducklings, the auditory information required for the call
preference to develop bears no relation to the adult call, and
is thus classed as non-specific. The cognitive mechanism
resulting from the interaction between an animal (even
before birth or hatching) and non-specific information from
the STE is termed *primal*, of which the mallard duckling
call preference is an example.

By contrast, cognitive structures resulting from exposure
to specific information from the STE are not primal but
products of learning: e.g., the ability of a baby to recognise
its mother's face in contrast to other faces requires exposure
to its mother's face.

Thus, in contrast to the nature-nurture error of explaining
a trait as 'genetic' or 'innate' without specifying environmental conditions and constraints, this framework allows
different classes of environmental constraint to be specified
as relevant (or not) to the emergence of a given trait, at any
stage of development.

The framework is also useful for avoiding the problems
identified by Oyama of thinking of development as the
result of some combination of two developmental processes,
the inherited and acquired, or 'mostly genetic' and 'mostly

environmental'. She argued that this compartmentalisation of causation is flawed because no criterion allows the specification of one kind of control or constraints without the other (p. 115). Johnson and Morton go further than Oyama because they show the *ways* in which genes and environment(s) are co-present and co-dependent for development to occur (Oyama's point), and may each provide sources of variation in the phenotype.

For example, variation can arise from:

(1) differences brought about by 'normal' variations within the genotype (e.g., height differences given similar nutrition and health);

(2) abnormal variations within the genotype (e.g., Down's syndrome);

(3) violation of the STE (e.g., language impairment in cases of neglect);

(4) variations in ISE (e.g., IQ as an outcome of interaction of the genotype with the ISE).

11

Constraints and Causes

From all this it becomes clear how destructive it is to isolate single, controlling causes for complex events. Nothing is brought into being by one single cause. For this reason, it is far more helpful to think of eventualities being brought into outcomes (into being what they are) by networks of constraint. We can obviously continue to recognize and specify that there are active and proximate causes of eventualities while still insisting on the fact that, in the case of a complex transformation of energy, there will be many contingent constraints which would need to be specified if a full account is to be given of what brought that eventuality into being.

If we fail to remember this (if, that is, we look for single causes rather than constraints) in accounting for complex phenomena, we usually end up by becoming competitive about the priority of the cause or causes that we have isolated from what is, in fact, a much more complicated network of constraint. Life is too short to specify the whole range of constraint which has controlled an eventuality into its outcome — into its being whatever it is that is making a demand on our attention. We therefore 'pick out' a single cause or set of causes to explain why a particular appearance or event has come into being, leaving tacit or assumed the many other relevant constraints (some of which may be themselves actively and directly causative, others of which may be passive, in the sense that they set

96

boundary conditions). We are then well on the way to an inappropriate, as opposed to a legitimate, reductionism.

The point is that all explanation of complex phenomena necessarily simplifies. But, who decides when, and on what grounds, an explanation is adequate? One pervasive claim (and one that underlies both Wilson's and Dawkins' accounts of human nature) rests on a belief that true explanation is that which reduces explanation to an underlying scientific law. In that case, the personal experience of any individual may have interest in terms of biography, but it is irrelevant to an explanation of what is fundamentally going on. At the opposite extreme are those who maintain that, in the human case, all explanation must at least include personal explanation. The gap that opens up here is as wide as the chasm that Kroeber (p. 16) claimed between anthropology and biology. Indeed, it is an update on the geography of the same chasm. The gap here is between, on the one side, the quest to extend explanations of a natural science, law-like type, to all phenomena, including human behaviours, and, on the other, the determination to give space to the idiosyncracies of conscious choice in contingently unrepeatable circumstances. By way of example, the 'chasm' can be observed between the two widely influential anthropologists, Radcliffe-Brown and Evans-Pritchard. On the one side, Radcliffe-Brown believed that a 'science (i.e., scientific account) of human behaviour' must be concerned not simply with description or with history, but with generalizable laws: from what is observed in particular societies, the general forms of social life can be deduced. Evans-Pritchard, in contrast, believed that the thought patterns of other peoples (in his case, the Nuer and the Azande) are internally coherent and correct, even though they include elements that we would regard as erroneous (for example, the causative power of magic). In his view, 'Social anthropology studies societies as moral or symbolic systems, and not as natural systems.'

The first endeavour is known as 'nomothetic' (from the Greek *nomos*, 'law'). Radcliffe-Brown stated explicitly that 'Social Anthropology . . . is a theoretical or nomothetic study of which the aim is to provide acceptable generalisation.' The second approach is known as 'hermeneutic' (from the Greek god Hermes, who carried messages). Nomothetic explanations tend to look for covering laws that lie behind contingent idiosyncracies; hermeneutic explanations look for (amongst much else) the inherent meanings in situations, or circumstances, or people as belonging to the explanation of a particular outcome. To revert to an example which I discussed in *The Sense of God* (p. 18), 'Why did Caesar go to the Senate?', where he was to be murdered. According to the hermeneutic explanation of Shakespeare, 'the cause was in his will'. The nomothetic explanation, though, looks for some general law in the background whereby, when circumstances A obtain, and there is no sufficient opposition, outcome B will occur. As a generalization, when dictators pass a specifiable threshold of self-aggrandizement, and the self-interest of powerful surrounding figures is no longer engaged, assassinations will occur or be attempted.

Transferring this to the gene-based claims for the explanation of human behaviour, we can see how obviously they fall on the nomothetic side of the chasm. As we have seen repeatedly, they look for covering laws which account for all human behaviours, even though the chain (or leash) of explanation may be a long one. In the case of Dawkins, he has accepted that the leash is so long that it would be wiser to think of *two* replicators, not one — memes as well as genes. However, there is no mistaking the nomothetic ambition of his work, which sits securely and uncritically in the positivist, covering law camp: genes have a tendency to produce gene-survival machines, provided countervailing factors do not intervene.

However, the weakness of this type of explanation is that it reduces rapidly to tautology. Bodies are gene-survival machines because genes are the sorts of things that produce gene-survival machines, provided nothing intervenes, and bodies are what genes produce, therefore bodies are gene-survival machines. The advantage of tautology to a passionate person (and Dawkins is nothing if not passionate) is that it tells us nothing that is not contained in the sentence in the first place — it certainly tells us nothing about belief in God — but it lends itself to slogans and to shouting, since there is nothing more to do with a tautology than to go on repeating it, which is exactly what Dawkins does, in a progressively louder voice.

It is also the reason why it is impossible to argue rationally with Dawkins (as those who have attempted to do so have found), because you can no more persuade a tautologist that he is simply repeating himself than you can persuade a solipsist (rationally) that he is wrong. No matter how often you ask him to kick a stone, there is no way that you can persuade him rationally that he is not constructing the experience in his own mind. In a comparable way, the deep commitment of Dawkins to irrationality (at least in the case of God) is obscured by his appeal to perfectly valid data in the domain of genetics; but his attempt to derive and apply a covering law argument from the data by way of analogy in order to account for culture remains, nevertheless, tautologically empty of content: brains are meme-survival machines because memes are the sorts of things requiring meme-survival machines (provided nothing intervenes), and brains are what memes require, therefore, brains are meme-survival machines.

In contrast to these extremes (i.e., between nomothetic and hermeneutic explanations of human behaviour), it seems obvious that what is required is an adequate specification or description of the underlying constraints which have, with some immediacy, brought about the phenomenon to be explained. The point about 'some immediacy' is that some limit must be set on the specification of constraint, since otherwise, we will be explaining everything by everything. *But*, there are no general rules which determine in advance what, in each instance, we must specify. If, as loss adjusters for an insurance firm, we ask, 'What caused that fire?', we are unlikely to specify, 'The presence of oxygen'. Yet, if we are evaluating the outbreak of fire in a space capsule, we will undoubtedly want to include the presence of oxygen in the specification of constraint.

At the same time, the list of *possible* constraints is not

limitless. Some are frivolous, even though they may have been believed to be causative in the past. Thus, a character in one of Aristophanes' plays maintains that rain is caused by Zeus urinating through a sieve. As an explanation, it certainly has *something* going for it: it accounts for the irregularity of rainfall and the space between the drops; and, in early Judaism, there was an attempt to measure the space between drops and to calculate what size of holes there must be in the canopy of the sky for rain to fall in that way. Observation rules out many claims and supplies a basis on which Ockham's razor can be applied. Thus, if goldfish are disappearing from your pond, it makes more sense to look for cats or herons than for fish-loving angels or visitors from outer space.

But the point still remains: the observable and/or specifiable network of constraints over human behaviour is, as a matter of fact, extremely large, and, while *some* proposed constraints may be excised as frivolous (or, indeed, as false), many, belonging to personal history, contingency and consciousness, cannot. The ambition to find covering laws which eliminate the need to specify any of those other constraints in accounting for human behaviour (i.e., strong reductionism) will never be fulfilled. This can be seen most obviously in the futility of yet another standard debate — the distinction between 'Why?' questions and 'How?' questions.

On the nomothetic side, it is usual to state that science answers 'How?' and not 'Why?' questions, such as 'Why is there something rather than nothing?' For many scientists of a positivist inclination, it is a non-question. What we take to be the universe is simply here as it is, and we are restricted, if we are wise, to trying to understand how it happens as it does. Dawkins is particularly aggressive in dismissing 'Why?' questions:

Darwin has shown a sequence of historical events — natural selection — which leads to the existence of all the apparently purposeful things like us. Asking 'Why?' in this case is the same as asking 'How?' That is, I believe, the only explanation — the only question — we're entitled to ask. Suppose that some child is dying of cancer, we say, 'Why is this child dying?' What has it done to deserve it?' The answer is, there's no reason why. It's not divine retribution. It's not due to sin. There is no reason other than a series of historical accidents which have led to this child dying of cancer. No reason to ask why.

The Daily Telegraph, 31 August, 1992, p. 11.

'Theirs not to reason why . . . .' Yet, in fact, to account for the Charge of the Light Brigade, the question 'Why?' is indispensable. No search for a covering law in the domain of genes and cultural context will supply a causative explanation of *how* the six hundred died, let alone why. The truth is that both *questions* are legitimate in the search for causative explanations of human behaviour, although not all *answers* (obviously) are salient or correct. Whether Dawkins likes it or not, the causes of human behaviour are widely diverse, and include the decision-making processes of the human will. That is why it is wiser to look for the specification of constraints, even though, in practice, one will often isolate particular causes from the entire network which have an immediate and direct bearing on an outcome with which one happens to be concerned — for example, the onset of cancer.

Yet, even in such a case, the 'Why?' questions are by no means so absurdly irrelevant to understanding as Dawkins supposes. *Why* does a particular form of cancer occur in identifiable populations? *Why* does AIDS spread in heterosexual populations in Africa with the speed that it does? We know (or think we know) *how* it spreads, but the *why* can only be answered by including cultural attitudes and behaviours, and personal decisions. The causative role of a virus in producing the outcome of AIDS may be established (supposing it is), but this is not the end of understanding.

Thus to say all this, while it rules out the crude reductive imperialism of Dawkins, is not in the least to deny the directly causative nature of genetic constraints. This is obvious from the fact that more than four thousand disorders have so far been identified which have a genetic base. But, even then, those disorders do not follow exactly the same trajectory in the life-history of each individual affected; there is more to be said in each case. True, there are, as Benjamin Franklin observed, two things that are inevitable in this life — taxes and death — and many gene-based disorders do follow a pathway to death within parameters that can be predicted. But, this does not make irrelevant all else that has been occurring and that is to occur in the life-history of a developing person or process.

It follows, therefore, that, in a developmental process, even the causative contributions of gene-transcription are not going to follow an invariable pathway within that process. As we have seen, what the genes transcribe, and when, is affected by changes in the environment (of cell, body, and context) in which they occur. Suppose that an error in gene-transcription leads to the specification of cells multiplying out of control, to some form of cancer: even then, there is not only one, single and inevitable history that ensues in the affected organism. It all depends; but depends on what? On so much that it would be impossible to specify: on the state of the organism, on the medical environment, on attitude, on prayer. To give a precise example: a recent study by Dr Michael King of 300 acutely ill patients (*Social Science and Medicine*, 1994) established that those in this sample with the strongest religious faith were less likely to recover than those with weaker beliefs. As he observed (and as Socrates observed in general long before him), 'Perhaps death is not the worst thing that can happen to them.'

So the fact that there is a high degree of reliability in observing the course and consequences of a particular cancer does not mean that there are not equally causative and reliable contributions to the developmental process of particular organisms, all of which affect each other in such a way that the contributions themselves may become modified. In accounting for particular outcomes, we need to be sensitive to much wider networks of constraint, the components of which are *not* always and invariably in the same relationship to each other.

Once again, the point is obvious: when we are trying to explain such a complicated phenomenon as 'human nature' (which is, in any case, not something 'out there' waiting to be described, but is, like much else, a human construction), we will always be wiser to think of sets of *constraints*, even if we wish to isolate some among them as being proximate causes of particular outcomes. An explanation will then be an adequate specification of those constraints which have brought about the eventuality in question. However, if we keep causes in the context of constraints, then we remain open to the reality that outcomes (that which presents itself evidentially before us) are brought into being, not by one cause or even by two (genes and culture) coercing the consequence, but, rather, by elaborate networks of constraint, some of which can only be uncovered by the very process of the investigation itself. The physicist Richard Feynmann used to insist that his physics students should always begin by asking themselves 'Why?' questions (note the contrast to Dawkins) about the world they experience:

> Learn by trying to understand simple things in terms of other ideas — always honestly and directly. What keeps the clouds up, why can't I see stars in the daytime, why do colours appear on oily water, what makes the lines on the surface of water being poured from a pitcher, why does a hanging lamp swing back and forth — all the innumerable little things you see all around you. Then when you have learned what an explanation really is, you can then go on to more subtle questions.
>
> Quoted from J. Gleick, *Genius: Richard Feynmann and modern physics*, London, Little, Brown, 1992, p. 357.

Unfortunately, 'learning what an explanation really is' is an exceptionally elusive and difficult task. So, too, with 'cause'. The simplest relationships are not difficult to isolate, even if only as examples of sufficient constancies of conjunction — rain causes wetness, fire causes warmth, ice causes you to slip and fall over, and so on — so it would seem obvious to continue; genes cause cystic fibrosis, culture causes haircuts in one style rather than another. However, even in those apparently simple instances, there is a much wider network of 'cause' bringing those eventualities into their outcome: why is it ice and not fire that causes you to slip, and why fall rather than fly, and why you at this particular moment? In fact, if we wish to specify what it is that has delivered you into a particular predicament, we would have to specify such an elaborate network of constraint that we would never, in practice, have time to complete the task. The cause of your falling goes down eventually into the laws of motion; it extends contingently to details of your own life-history, which cannot be repeated in any other instance. So, in practice, we select the constraints which we believe will provide reasons (sufficient reasons) to account for the outcome. Ockham's razor (p. 84) has virtue so long as you do not use it to cut off your own head: where additional constraints *must* be specified in order to account for an eventuality, nothing is gained by insisting, in the name of Ockham, on only one. A better principle is this: be sufficiently, but not recklessly, generous in the specification of constraints; or at least otherwise be modest in what you claim to be 'the true and only explanation'.

For the complexity gets even greater. Even when we accept that all behaviours and events are constrained into their outcome by elaborate networks of constraint, it does not follow that the items in those networks operate in the same way at all moments. Thus, some constraints are passive, and are simply setting the boundary conditions of possibility; others are permissive, allowing the possibility of outcome, but requiring some further sequence in the developmental process to be activated, others are active, operating as direct causes on a particular outcome, but not in isolation from the other constraints. But constraints do not remain in the same state at all moments of a developmental history. They may, for example, move from being passive to active. Still, in the case of biology, the task is, as Pattee states it, 'to explain the origin and operation (including the reliability and persistence) of the hierarchical constraints which harness matter to perform coherent functions' (H. H. Pattee, 'Laws and Constraints, Symbols and Language', C. H. Waddington, ed., *Towards a Theoretical Biology*, IV, Edinburgh University Press, 1972, p. 248).

Of course, put like that, the task of explanation clearly

becomes impossible. There is no way in which we could specify the entire network of relevant constraint in the case of each and every outcome: it would mean accounting for one thing by everything. Not surprisingly, therefore (to repeat the same point), we separate out the task of explanation, by attending to the word 'adequate' — an *adequate* description of those causes that have brought about the eventuality in question. This involves selecting from the whole network of constraint those items that relate specifically (specifiably) to the question we have in mind. The questions may be physical, chemical, biological, historical, cultural, sociological, genetic, biographical, medical, ethical, all the way through to gossip in the pub. In each case, we isolate from the entire network of existing constraint those items which we take to be directly causative in producing the outcome.

If we are then exhilarated by the explanatory success of what we have isolated (for example, if it seems recurrent across human examples, if it seems almost invariably linked to outcomes, if it allows predictions, and so on), we may then lose our heads (as Dawkins and Wilson do), and suppose that we have found 'the cause' of human nature: however complex and idiosyncratic individual histories may be, they are nothing but variations on the basic theme of x-into-y — in the sociobiological case, of 'genes-into-phenotypes', in the case of the Dawkins' 'virus analogy', of 'memes into human behaviour'. In fact, any phenotype is a consequence of a developmental process in which much more is interacting than genes and culture. Phenotypes are a tangle of interior and exterior relationships; they require both genes and culture to be what they are (both being always in the network of constraint), but they are not the consequence of *only* genes and culture in all the eventualities of their history.

If, then, we begin to think of human life as a developmental process, we can see that the constraints of genes and culture do not impose a pre-planned order on otherwise chaotic material, dictating behaviours to it. This is exactly the presupposition of innumerable TV documentaries, especially those on sexuality, which point a camera at the

mating behaviours of other species, and infer that we are
those behaviours 'writ large' — what one may, with justice,
call 'the ethological fallacy'. In contrast, genes and culture
form a necessary part (but only a part) of the network of
constraint that prepares the human organism for behaviours which take degrees of control over its own outcomes
within the boundaries of constraint.

It is precisely this which creates the freedom of human
nature to transcend the biological and cultural points of its
departure: constraint is the condition of freedom. This is
exactly the opposite of what E. O. Wilson supposes. In his
view, all behavioural sciences will be subordinated to
sociobiology (because sociobiology supplies the most fundamental causes of human behaviour), and human nature
will be 'grounded':

> If the brain is a machine of ten billion nerve cells and the
> mind can somehow be explained as the summed activity of
> a finite number of chemical and electrical reactions, bound-
> aries limit the human prospect — we are biological and our
> souls cannot fly free.
>
> *On Human Nature*, p. 1.

It hardly needs pointing out that, even if both parts of the
protasis could be established, the apodosis does not follow.
In fact, as I have often pointed out in other books, on the
basis of both cybernetics and biology, the notion of constraint is not negative and restricting; it is the necessary
condition of freedom. To quote Ashby's version of the cybernetic principle: 'Where a constraint exists, advantage can
usually be taken of it' (see *Licensed Insanities*, p. 102).
Even more advantage can be taken of it by an organism
that has conscious understanding of it: our souls *do* fly free,
and can *only* fly free, because there is a complicated network of constraint that produces the kind of brain which
humans happen to have — that is, a sufficiently large
number of chemical and electrical reactions of the kind that
are held within the boundaries of the brain. The interior
experiences on the basis of these reactions are of such a
consistent kind that they evoke the language of mind and

of soul, and if we did not use *this* language, we would have to invent another to do justice to the data. This will remain the case even when the so-called brain-browser has created for humans (as it has nearly done for rats) a three-dimensional map of how the brain is organized and what each part does — for all the reasons about constraint already given at length.

12

Conclusion: Human Nature and God

'Evil: Is It Born Or Is It Bred?' So asked a headline in *The Independent on Sunday* (21 February, 1993). It was asking the question of the two young boys who had murdered James Bulger in a particularly grim and horrifying way. It is an exact example of the fallacy of the falsely dichotomous question (see *Licensed Insanities*, p. 101), arising from the fundamentally mistaken ways of describing gene-culture coevolution that we have been examining — the basic model, which sees two sources of cause coercing human nature into its outcome. What *drove* (the causal explanation of force, derived from one of two sources) two young people to the abduction and murder of a young child?

To take this example is not to trivialize a great tragedy, it is to underline that our assumptions about what forms human nature, and how it does so, become the anthropology (the account of human nature and behaviour) which forms our attitudes, our policies, our moral thought and action. The headline is a classic example of the totally dominating way in which the exploration of human behaviour has now come to be set: nature or nurture? Genes or culture? Innate or acquired? Where genes are concerned, the view that genes cause and determine character has gone deeply into popular assumption. To give only one example, Maureen Long, in a book on the effects of post-abortion trauma

(*Right to Choose?*, Christian Focus Publications Ltd, 1993) wrote:

> Modern science tells us that we are human and unique from conception. At that point, a special blueprint, only as big as a pinhead, unseen by the naked eye, unfolds a spectacular sequence of events like a computer programme, that determines who and what we are. At that moment the eventual size of our adult feet, the colour of our hair and eyes, our height and our natural tastes in music, our talents and our potentialities are determined.
>
> p. 163.

As we have seen, nothing could be more false. At the opposite extreme stand those who attribute everything to the will and to human choice. Thus, *The Independent on Sunday* gave a number of responses to its question, including that of Mr John Patten, who, at the time, was the Secretary of State for Education:

> It is, to me, self-evident that we are born with a sense of good and evil. It is also self-evident that as we grow up each individual chooses whether to be good or bad. Fear of eternal damnation was a message reinforced through attendance at church every week. The loss of that fear has meant a critical motive has been lost to young people when they decide whether to try to be good citizens or to be criminals.

The truth is that a correlation between belief in hell and good behaviour has not been established. Students at Cambridge in the days when they undoubtedly did believe in hell did less work and caused far more uproar in the town than do students now, who do not, by and large, believe in hell, but who produce more essays, fewer illegitimate babies, and much more support for those less fortunate than themselves.

However, the more important point is that Mr Patten is precisely illustrating the point made at the outset, that once you get yourself trapped in this 'interactive frame' — asking whether it is born or bred or some combination of both — you end up with generalized solutions which depend on what weighting you give in the interaction. What is 'self-evident' to one is not so to another; and policy continues to oscillate from one side of the interaction to the other.

In contrast, we can now envisage a post-modernist anthropology which mediates the new insights and does justice to the human sense of value, instead of regarding it dismissively as an adjunct of the genes.

To clear the ground to begin with, it is clear that we are not born with '*a sense*' of anything like 'good and evil'. We are born as a developing process, in which the structures of the brain (themselves still, at birth, with considerable development ahead of them) prepare us for characteristic behaviours. These include the human universals of judgement — of discrimination between up and down, right and left, dark and light. However, because we live towards a future of which we are conscious, but of which we know virtually nothing — witness the seven (subsequently six) wise men advising the Chancellor of the Exchequer — we are compelled to *evaluate* projected actions. In other words, we develop value systems of judgement, of right and wrong, of wise and foolish, of good and evil.

At this level, we are not talking about some universal *content*. What counts as good or evil may differ widely from one culture to another, or even within the lifetime of an individual. We learn what counts as a value through the process of life. If some of these values turn out to transcend cultural boundaries, it is not because they are delivered to us with the morning milk; they have to be learned and acquired. However, because human life is set within non-negotiable constraints, which alone make it possible, it becomes apparent (and, increasingly, universally agreed) what it is that belongs to human flourishing, or as Aristotle called it, *eudaimonia*. Ethics will never be as coercive as the judgement of colour. As Aristotle put it, a child moves from command to consent, from *epagoge* to *nous*. But the fact remains that we do recognize goodness (as well as truth and beauty), and know how to use the word 'good' with reliability — though not without mistakes and not without considerable differences in content between different cultures, or different historical periods, or different people, or even different stages of one's own life. So far as content is concerned, acculturation clearly plays a large part. But the fact that the *judgement* is universal points back to a brain-competence to which, no doubt, the genes make their necessary contribution. Thus, what *is* universal (or near-universal) in the human case is the underlying structure of judgement.

The brain, therefore, does not start from nowhere. Extremely stable developmental processes, involving genes and other interactants, prepare it for characteristic behaviours. Some of these may well have an ethological connection, though perhaps not as precisely as Paul Maclean, for example, has argued. In his view, one can do a kind of evolutionary archaeology of the triune brain, identifying the stages at which the evolving brain was, so to speak, laid down — the reptilian brain, the palaeomammalian brain, which includes the limbic system, and the neomammalian, with the reptilian complex and the limbic system contributing what he calls 'basic animality' (in J. W. Bowker, ed., *Origins, Functions and Management of Aggression in Biocultural Evolution, Zygon*, XVIII, 1983, p. 369). But still, the fact remains that we share about 98.4 per cent of our genes with the higher primates, and it is surely the case that the genes, via the proteins, contribute to and constrain the formation of the structures of our brains. These prepare us for behaviours many of which are immediate and unwilled — for example, the 'four Fs of survival' of the limbic system (feeding, fighting, fleeing, and sexual reproduction): they are essential to our safety, but they can precipitate us into attitudes and behaviours of which, in our more reflective moments, we might be deeply ashamed. The ethological fallacy (p. 106) remains a fallacy, but it has this virtue, that it reminds us how deeply our behaviours are embedded in the unchosen and the unwilled.

The same point is reinforced by the fact that we are born into families, societies, geographies, historical circumstances which we did not choose, but which certainly set constraints on our behaviours — again, on occasion, controlling us into attitudes and behaviours which, on reflection (or from some other standpoint), seem simply wrong.

In both these major ways, from birth and from the environment, major religions, both East and West, have recognized that in our condition, and in at least some of our behaviours, 'the evil that I do' (or that I am) in part precedes me: *I* did not choose my genes or my environment and, yet, to some extent, they create that 'what I am' with which we began, as a question (p. 3). Of course, these religions knew nothing, until recently, about genes, but they knew about the continuities of life from one generation to another, which mean that we are not born as 'beautiful, blank sheets of white paper'. Christianity talks about the *reatus*, the real condition of aberrancy, in terms of original sin, though it would be better expressed as aboriginal sin; and this is an unwilled, unchosen condition, distinct from the *actus* of sinful things that we do, or say, or intend. Eastern religions speak of karma or *kamma*, which, again, precedes us from earlier births — though here, it is true, the accumulation of fault did pertain to choice in those earlier lives.

The implication is obvious: human character and behaviour are controlled *in part* into their outcomes by constraints which precede us, and which we did not choose. Again, *in part*, these behaviours are, to say the least, self-assertive and antisocial. That is why Freud could propose a dynamic of psychological formation which recognizes that, in some respects, we all set out from what he called 'abject points of departure'.

Yet, it is obvious that most people, *normally*, transcend those abject points of departure. The word 'normally' has to be stressed as a reminder that norms are statistical: the 'abnormal' is exactly what the underlying Latin points to, 'that which stands away from' the statistical norms, a point to which we will return. The transcendence of our abject points of departure is the process of growing through life, a process that continues, normally, through and beyond even the university of the third age. On the eve of his hundredth birthday, the last survivor of the War Poets of the First World War, Geoffrey Dearmer, looked at a new edition of his poems and said, 'Did I really write that? Oh dear, it's really quite bad: the overwritten work of a young man using important words without justification' (*The Daily Telegraph*, 23 February, 1993, p. 7). At the time, it was surely the best that he could do: we transcend the points of our departure, or can do, given the unpredictable constraints which have yet to delimit the unfolding of our own developmental process. Part of the process is a matter of choice, as Mr Patten supposed, but part is not. Many of the constraints on the developmental process remain non-negotiable and often, in any case, opaque to the introspection of our rational choice.

Nevertheless, the key to policy is the recognition that while our points of departure are, at least in some respects, abject, we can and do transcend them. The limbic system may precipitate us into fighting or into fleeing, as an immediate reaction, but we are capable of, so to speak, 'getting on top' of the system and directing our subsequent behaviour, which means that, in vital ways, we are agents of many of our actions, just as we are subjects of our own experience. This, too, belongs to the 'what I am' of human nature. Within the boundaries of constraint, it is I, myself, who have the opportunity of transcending the points of my departure. Any parent, teacher, social worker can know and observe this happening every day. If we are not, in the institutions of society, providing the endorsement and reinforcement of this evocation of transcendence, so that it does indeed become 'the right choice' where each one of us is concerned, then we are subverting the truth of human anthropology — what it is that makes us human. To be human in this respect is to acquire, and to accept responsibility for one's own actions and thoughts; to be human socially is to create and sustain the circumstances in which this responsibility can be exercised (for a practical application of this vital point, see my paper written for a UN working party, 'The Religious Understanding of Human Rights and Racism', in D. D. Honoré, ed., *Trevor*

Huddleston: Essays on his Life and Work, Oxford University Press, 1988, pp. 153–73).

What seems to make this difficult at the present time is that we live at the end of at least three centuries in which a real struggle has been taking place to secure the maximum freedom for individuals to do exactly what Mr Patten wants, to make choices within the boundary of law — what I have called 'a preferential option for options' (see further p. 186). Maybe we are recognizing that some options, even within the law, are contradictory to the transcendence of our abject points of departure, and may, in fact, reinforce at least some people in behaviours that would normally count as wrong or, indeed, as evil. An instance would be the contest between freedom from censorship and the increasing levels of violence in films and videos, with the inevitable uncertainty in between about whether such films are cathartic or reinforcing. The uncertainty *is* inevitable, because you can never run negative controls on individual human behaviour. Thus, we cannot rerun a human life in order to know what it would have been like if it had followed an alternative line of action — ten years spent watching video nasties, and then ten years not doing so. Successive decades with alternative trials tell us nothing, since in a developmental process, the first option becomes an embedded experience and memory in relation to the second; and no control group can be established because the variables are too great. Given the extreme and often institutionalized violence of the twentieth century, it is not surprising that we explore, through the instruments of public reflection, what it is and how it arises — through books, films, videos, even through the ethological fallacy itself, that we are nothing but 'nature red in tooth and claw' acting out our natural predisposition; that we are nothing but gene-survival machines, simply expressing the strategies of the selfish gene. Such views are simply wrong, no matter how widely they are accepted. But just to refute such error is not enough. Where, in our society, is the comparable exploration and endorsement of the powers that make us human?

To achieve that, we would have to gain confidence together in a far more truthful anthropology, and one which does justice to this central fact: even general constraints in the domain of genetics or biology or social context are always constraints on a developmental process, and they will not produce the same outcome in every case. John Major may think that crime is a consequence of socialist-run inner cities, but not everyone in an inner city is constrained into the outcome of crime. The way in which events and opportunities occur to us depends on the developmental history that each one of us has had. There is no deterministic relationship between event A and consequence B, either way around. Event A might be the restoration of capital punishment, but it will not have a deterministic consequence B that another small boy will never again be murdered; event A might be the removal of poverty in the inner cities, but it will not have a deterministic consequence B that crime will diminish in some predictable proportion. What we do and how we behave depends on our own developmental history, on the circumstances and on the resources available to us. If we make generalizations, as politicians clearly have to do, the most they can do is exhibit norms, and norms are statistical. They do not exhibit what causes the abnormal — that which stands away from the statistical norms, nor, in themselves, can they say anything about the reinforcement of those constraints which control our process of growth in the direction of transcendence. It is ab-normal in the extreme for humans to be incapable of operating distinctions between good and evil — so abnormal that we isolate them with the label 'psychopath', though that label in itself tells us nothing about what has constrained such people into this outcome.

Is, then, God a virus? It must seem that we have strayed far from the question. Yet, in fact, not so. We have already seen that the simple answer to that question is 'No', because the analogy between genes and memes is too imprecise to be any help in understanding the transmission of cultural items or information. But the more serious point lies beyond. Once we see that the process of human life is controlled into its outcome (into its being what it is) by an extremely elaborate network of constraint, then we cannot rule out, on some *a priori* grounds, the possibility that the consequence of God operates constantly within these networks of constraint. You may say, like Laplace in a Newtonian universe of explanation, 'I have no need of that hypothesis'; and you may say exactly the same, as do Wilson and Dawkins, standing in a neo-Darwinian universe of explanation. In both those cases, though, we are talking about the adequacy of explanation for particular eventualities: the rise and fall of tides, the origin of species. The mistake has always been (so far) the belief that each limited specification of constraint, because it is so adequate and powerful in its own domain, can be extended so that no other or additional constraints need ever be specified in accounting for different — or even for the same — eventualities. The failure to recognize this is a reason why the nature/nurture debate has been so bad-tempered — each side has wanted to give the whole account.

However, once it is recognized that the networks of constraint which bring about or sustain eventualities in being are always larger than we can specify, it becomes clear that we cannot eliminate God from inclusion within them (or as the source and guarantor of them) on the *a priori* ground that science does not allow it. The Christian doctrine of creation is one of relationship and of God's continuing sustenance of that to which he is related as the unproduced Producer of all that is. This means at once that adequate (i.e., adequate in the heuristic sense described above) explanations of particular phenomena or events will clearly not need to specify God, even if God is a constant constraint over all eventualities without exception. How or why did I raise my hand? Adequate explanations need only specify the proximate and relevant constraints, which might be related to many different interests and will, accordingly, be different in what they specify. Thus, one might be interested in muscle contraction, or class-room behaviour in a school, or in the rules of umpiring at cricket.

For an adequate explanation in the domain of science, there will be no need to specify the constraint of God, even if we allow that God is a constant constraint, sustaining all things in being. At the same time, though, it remains possible for us, if we wish, to realize the constraint of God in a particular way over the outcomes in our own behaviours, by the faith that it can be so — as Jesus so repeatedly insisted. Indeed, the consistency with which Jesus made the constraint of God specific and continuous in relation to his own humanity is precisely why Christians speak of the Incarnation and of two natures in one person — the constraint of God constantly and consistently present within the whole network of constraint, in a way that does not obliterate the humanity to which it is unceasingly present, and in which it is always realized. Where we are concerned, the difference, in classical terms, is that which obtains between the primary causality of God in creation, which sustains all things in being, and the secondary causality, which is operated through us who have been created in such a way that we can become delegated constraints of God through grace in the acquiescence of faith. In a different theological system (that of Islam), it is the value of the doctrine of kasb/iktisab, of acquisition. While the constant constraint of God may, indeed, be a necessary condition of there being a universe at all, the degrees of human freedom open up the responsibility of human choices; there is no compulsion to actualize the constraint of God at the level of secondary causality. But, where this constraint *is* actualized, the consequences are so clearly predicted that the distinction between true and false claims to that condition can be identified; by their fruits shall you know them; and the fruits of the Spirit are not much differentiated between religions, as we shall see.

The actualization of the constraint of God is, in practice, the making specific of God as constraint, or, in more traditional language, it is the constant practice of the presence of God, of God as constraint over the outcomes of our behaviour, moving them constantly in the direction of love. The realization of God is grounded in prayer, meditation, contemplation, worship, in word and sacrament, and it is extended in actions of love, which flow forth from the constraint of God over our lives. And as all evolutionary advance is constrained by future conditions of which it knows nothing — and this is what is known as 'downward' or 'backward' causation — so our lives also are constrained by the future condition of God, of that final transcendence of the process which has brought us to this conclusion, in the vision of God and in the company of all the saints.

And that returns us, finally, to John Clare. The developmental process of his life carried him into the bereft experience of the County Asylum. No one, perhaps, would choose it as a way to go — 'the vast shipwreck of my life's esteems'. Yet, he remains who he is, not other than himself or less than himself, still open to the transcendent process that Christians understand as our atonement with God:

> I long for scenes where man has never trod;
>   A place where woman never smiled or wept;
> There to abide with my Creator, God,
>   And sleep as I in childhood sweetly slept;
> Untroubling and untroubled where I lie; —
> The grass below — above the vaulted sky.

But this leaves large questions unanswered. In particular, it fails to answer both Wilson's and Dawkins' question of why it is that religions exhibit such appalling histories and evil behaviours. Dawkins is so unequivocally wrong about memes and 'God as a virus' that we may dismiss as equally erroneous the angry passion against religion which leads him into his mockery and malice. But we then ignore the fact that his protest is well-grounded in truth — maybe not the whole truth, but in truth, nevertheless. Why *are* religions so dangerous that they may well destroy human life on this planet as we know it? A major part of the answer lies, as we can now go on to see, in the relation of religions to the conditions of body-culture coevolution.

PART II

Why Are Religions So Dangerous?

13

Religions and Conflict

'In the summer of 1981, people in the United Kingdom woke up one Sunday morning to headlines exactly two inches high in the *News of the World*: 'BLOOD ON OUR STREETS'. It was the first of a number of serious race riots, followed by others in Toxteth, Moss Side, and Wood Green.

It was not the only depressing news in that week: it included the failure of a peace initiative in Afghanistan, the death of another hunger striker in Northern Ireland, the withdrawal of the Commission for Justice and Peace, and the shooting of a fifteen-year-old boy. There were executions in the aftermath of the Beheshti assassination in Iran, including the reported executions of children on the grounds (according to Ayatollah Gilani as reported) that in Islamic law a nine-year-old girl is mature and responsible. During that week the trial concluded in West Germany of a number of concentration camp guards, and the sentencing of Kurt Ashe took place — Belgium's Eichmann as he was described, who, as a 'desk murderer', was responsible for the death of 26,000 Belgian Jews.

It was the week also of Gromyko's threatening visit to Poland, and of the Israeli politicians looking for a viable coalition, with a virtual tie between Mr Begin's Likud party and Labour. The odds at the time were on Mr Begin succeeding, and it was predictable that the religious parties (the NRP and the Agudat Israel) would set as a price for their cooperation the extension of Israeli settlements on the West Bank.

All in all, it was not a good week for optimists — given that an optimist is someone who proclaims that this is the best of all possible worlds, and a pessimist agrees. Reading and listening to the news that week brought to mind two lines from A. P. Herbert's *Two Gentlemen of Soho*:

Man, like a pebble in a glacier,
Moves imperceptibly, but always down.

What was overlooked by commentators at the time (as it usually is) is the fact that there is a common element in those very different items in the news: religion. That is not to say that religion is the single cause of the seemingly intractable problems in Northern Ireland, or between Israel and the Palestinians, or in the Philippines, or in the Lebanon; nor does it follow that religion is even the most important cause. It *is* to say that religious beliefs, and hopes, and memories are so important in these crises that we have to understand more clearly and more intelligently the part that religion plays.'

That long quotation comes from a Radio Three broadcast I made in that year, commenting on the events in that particular week. Looking back on the decade that has followed, we can see that the configurations of conflict have changed: Afghanistanis are engaged now in civil war, and Israel and the PLO have taken a step towards each other, not to grab each other by the throat, but to shake very tentative hands together, as they did on the lawn of the White House.

Many of the conflicts persist, however, and others have exploded into our midst; and that at least one of them is a conflict of religions (at least in connection) is brought home by the fact that reference is constantly made to Bosnian Muslims, though not, as it might be, to Catholic Croatians and Orthodox Serbs. At the very least, the religious affiliations of these peoples give to them an identity (and, as we shall see, much more than an identity) in a way that is entirely familiar in the case of Northern Ireland.

It is because religious commitments run so deep and issue so often in war and conflict, that I have spent a lifetime trying to understand why it is that religious people

hate each other so much, and why it is that religions are a
real threat to the future of human life as we know it. Let
me quote myself again, this time from the opening of the
BBC series on religions in the UK (later published as
Worlds of Faith, London, Ariel Books, 1983), which was
broadcast in 1983. I began by saying:

I suppose these programmes first began to take shape some
time in 1954. I was a young national serviceman in Nigeria,
and I remember very well the afternoon when I was sent
out to the local market-place to sort out a riot — not a race
riot but a religious riot. I was absolutely terrified. The trouble had begun because some people, who belonged to two
different religions, were fighting over a donkey. Why, I
haven't the slightest idea; and I don't think we ever found
out. But, while I stood there, trying to reason with them,
they literally pulled the donkey apart, limb from limb.

It was at that moment, standing there and looking at the
anger and hatred in those faces, that I set out on a journey
which has brought me to the beginning of these programmes. Much of my time since then has been spent trying
to understand what it is about religion which makes religious people so angry and passionate. Think how easily
those passions and emotions explode into violence: bombs
in Hyde Park and Ballykelly and many other parts of
Northern Ireland; the destruction of Beirut; the whole conflict over Israel/Palestine in the Near East; the bitter
divisions between black and white in the apartheid system
of South Africa; Cyprus; India and Pakistan; Poland; the
Philippines; Iran; Afghanistan. The list is almost endless.
Even while we were making the first programme, Sikhs
were rioting in India, and in Northern Nigeria 450 people
were killed in religious riots (p. 9).

Some of those examples are, of course, very dated and specific. But, here again, many of the conflicts mentioned still
persist, and others have been added to them. To take only
one, in Sri Lanka the uneasy coexistence — between
Tamils, who are mainly Hindu, and Singhalese, who are
mainly Buddhist — has flared into intercommunal violence
of a particularly intransigent kind; and, as I stated in

Licensed Insanities, we are observing here, not a recent (say, post-colonial) disturbance, but a conflict that goes back nearly two thousand years. Why, then, is there the unease? If we have lived with wars of religion for more than two thousand years, why do I use the extravagant language of a religious threat to the future of human life, at least as we know it now?

The answer is simply to reflect on how many of the countries involved in the conflicts just mentioned have nuclear weapons, or probably have nuclear weapons but are not admitting it, or make it clear that they would have nuclear weapons if they could. Add to this the simpler (in terms of production) possibilities of chemical and biological weapons, and it may become more obvious why I feel there is some urgency. In 1988, a specific appeal was made to the Arab world that a chemical or biological counterpart to the Israeli nuclear deterrent should be produced; and Iraq has already used a chemical weapon against the Kurds.

Of course, if such weapons were only to serve as deterrents, then, perhaps, we should rejoice and be glad (we are, after all, now nearly half a century away from the last global conflict). But this kind of consideration is extremely unwise, in the religious case. All religions have eschatological scenarios of a cataclysmic kind (or, to put it in less technical jargon, they all envisage that the world, or this particular cycle of cosmic history, will end in destruction and chaos, and that this eventuality may not be long delayed): the birth-pangs of the Messiah, the second coming of Christ, and the *yaum udDin* in Islam are examples. Hindus believe that we are living in the Kali Yuga, Buddhists that we are in the *mappo*, both of which are the end of a cosmic cycle when evil and chaos prevail. If the cookie of the universe begins to crumble, religious people are not necessarily disturbed: it may be a fundamental confirmation of their beliefs; and their beliefs (as we will see) *may* require them to be the crumblers of the cookie.

Add (again) to all this, the fact that religious people characteristically believe that there are more important things in life than living, and that they would rather die than abandon their faith, and it becomes clear why I cry out as a voice, if not yet in the wilderness, then certainly in what will become a wilderness if we do not take religions a great deal more seriously in our attempts to unravel the major conflicts of our time. If we do not understand the interior dynamic of religious systems and religious lives, we have absolutely no chance whatsoever of understanding, let alone defusing, the conflicts which are already misery and desperation to many of those involved in them, and which are likely to destroy us all. I am *not* saying that religions are the sole cause of these conflicts; but they undoubtedly contribute to them.

But having got this far, it may well seem that all this is a grotesque overstatement of the case, for, surely, religions are the great reserves of spiritual currency, issuing notes which promise the bearers of human nature a just return when they present their account? And, even more than this, do they not demand certain clear standards of behaviour now? 'He hath shewed thee, O man, what is good; and what doth the Lord require of thee, but to do justly, and to love mercy, and to walk humbly with thy God.' So said the prophet Micah (6.8), but we can find comparable sentiments in virtually every religion, and it is by no means easy to tell, in each case, from which particular religion each of the following comes:

What does the law of life require, but to show justice to all, severity to self, service to the old, kindness to the young, generosity to the poor, good counsel to friends, forbearance with enemies, indifference to fools, respect to the learned and sincerity before God?

What is required of you is to injure none by thought or word or deed, to give to those in need and to be kind to all.

To respect others and to bear oneself with humility, to be peaceful and grateful, to attend to what is right at all times, this is the supreme blessing.

Blessed are the poor in spirit . . . , blessed are the gentle . . . , blessed are those who mourn . . . , blessed are those who hunger and thirst after uprightness . . . , blessed are the merciful . . . , blessed are the pure in heart . . . , blessed are the peacemakers.

To be human is the same throughout the world: it is to put into practice five virtues, courtesy, generosity, good faith, commitment, kindness.

The essence of the conduct of the one who knows the truth is that he causes no injury to anyone: to harm no one is true religion.

True religion is the inspiring of love. The One whom you love above all is in his people: to serve all people is to serve God, and it is through service that love is made real.

Surely this is what religion is about. One can make the same point even more briefly by observing that the Golden Rule, either in its positive or negative form, appears in all the major religions of the world. All religions require and endorse behaviours that are far removed from the hatred and hostility with which we began.

So, a central question is clearly this: what determines which voice prevails at any particular time or in any particular occasion of inter-religious encounter? The voice of service or the voice of strife, the voice of inclusion or the voice of exclusion? And, how does it come about that both of these appear in religious life and practice?

Nothing much is gained by saying that the involvement of religions in these particularly intransigent conflicts is not religion, but, rather, the abuse or exploitation of religion, that it is the harnessing of religious emotion, not religion itself which is involved. There is an extremely limited truth in this, but, even if it were more extensively true than it is, it would not help us to understand why it is religious people who are so often involved in the most brutal and hate-filled actions. For, it is often those who are held up as exemplary in their religious commitment who are capable of actions which, to those outside the religion (and often to others within it), seem most hideous. Take, for example, the attitude of Appar to the Jains. The Jains elevated ahimsa (non-violence) to such a height that the dedicated among them brush the path before their feet for fear of harming an insect in their path. In southern India, the Jains lived among ʿSaivites (devotees of ʿSiva). The ʿSaivites produced superb and moving poetry of bhakti (loving devotion to God). Appar, of the seventh century CE, was one of the great Nayanmars (sixty-three ʿSaivite 'saints'), and he poured his devotion into poetry:

> Subtle to find, yet present in the good,
> Present in word, in wind, in flame and burning wood,
> Present in sweetness and in shining light,
> In height, in depth, and in the fearful night:
> If I forget some once to sing your praise,
> Strike it from the record of my days.

Yet Appar had once been a convert to the Digambara sect of the Jains — he had even risen to be head of his community. But then he was reconverted, and he poured out his hate in his poems as well, against 'those weak and filthy Jains with their yellowing teeth'. It was a hatred shared by other ʿSaivites: their temple walls still record the massacre that ended the Jain presence in their midst, in which they took eight thousand Jains in Madurai and impaled them on stakes for speaking ill of ʿSiva.

When Emerson gave up preaching in 1828, he did so because he contemplated the unending theme of violence that runs through the history of religions:

> The history of persecution is a history of endeavours to cheat nature, to make water run uphill, to twist a rope of sand . . . . A mob is a society of bodies voluntarily depriving themselves of reason.

But since religion gives to many the appearance of being bereft of reason in the first place — religion, as it is said, being that which takes refuge in the unknowable from the terrors of the unknown — it is to them unsurprising that religious people put on the mask of the mob at the slightest drop of a dogma: a maniac is someone who says something absurd, and a religious maniac is someone who believes it.

Is it, then, the irrationality of the mob mentality that makes the encounters of different religions with each other seem to be as smooth and twinkling as a summer sea, on the surface, but, below, a sliding menace of predation and death, sinking down into a darkness that no rational light can penetrate? The public meeting of religions is double-handed: in the one hand, a ticket to the latest, lavish interfaith assembly — Global Forum or the World Parliament of Religions — where all will, unsurprisingly, vote in favour of goodness; and, in the other hand, a knife. Why is it, as I have asked the question before, and as Wilson and Dawkins are asking it as well, that religions are such bad news to those of whom they disapprove — women, homosexuals, heretics, animals, each other? Or to put it a bit more positively, why is it that the voices of inclusion, friendship and moral alliance are usually more evident in meetings than they are in practice in the world? Religions might themselves answer in single, simple words, and just say 'sin', or 'karma', or Kali Yuga; and it is certainly one of the merits of religions that they take sin and evil seriously. But, even so, we might still want to know why it is religious people who are, so often, so intransigent.

The paradox of religious urgency

To answer those questions, we need, first and above all else, to understand the paradox of religious urgency. The reason religions are such *bad* news is because they are such *good* news. There is a well-known saying that the reason academic disputes are so vicious is because the stakes are so low. The reason religious disputes are so vicious is because the stakes are so supernaturally, transcendentally, hypercosmically high. There is too much at stake for religions to be casual about the consequences of their encounters with each other.

What, then, does it mean to say that religions are such good news in human history? To take, first, only the most immediate and obvious point, religions are the resource and inspiration of virtually all the most enduring and value-laden human achievements: art, music, drama, dance, agriculture, poetry, ethics — all these have been created from specifically religious sources of inspiration and meaning. Even the natural sciences have their roots in religious inspiration. As with the 'bad news', so also here: it is not the case that religion has been the *only* source of these explorations of human possibility, but it has certainly been immensely powerful in bringing technique and beauty into birth, for it has not simply been a matter of inspiration, however loosely that word may be construed. It has also been a matter of patronage. In India, the patron who wishes to build a village or a temple is traditionally called yajamana, the one who performs sacrifice, since, in the Vedic imagination, the universe is understood as a process of constant transformation by way of sacrifice — a process of devouring, being devoured, and the relationship between the two. This is religion at the root of art because a work of art is (or should always be) a manifestation of the creative urgency of the universe itself, not an illustration of it. This is why artists or craftsmen, before starting on a particular work, lay out their instruments or tools, and worship them with incense, flowers, and unhusked rice: 'The tree which is to be felled by the carpenter or sculptor is propitiated with offerings; he lays his hand on it with a mantra, asking pardon of the spirits residing in the tree (*Brhatsamhita* 57.10–11). The axe which is to fell the tree is anointed with honey and butter so that the tree is not hurt when the transformation through which a shape of nature becomes a work of art is begun by the craftsman' (S. Kramrisch, *Exploring India's Sacred Art*, Philadelphia, University of Pennsylvania Press, 1983, p. 62). That is why, also, the uproar in the UK over the denunciation by Prince Charles of so much unsympathetic modern architecture might have been a great deal more serious in India. When King Bhoja compiled the *Samarangana-sutradhara* in the eleventh century, he imposed the death penalty on any architect who practised architecture without correct knowledge or in the arrogance of false self-certainty. An architect who does not understand the process of the universe and who ignores it, disturbs the universe in a sense even more profound than that epitomized in the epitaph for Vanbrugh: 'Lie heavy on him, Earth, for he / Laid many a heavy load on thee'.

Religion, though, is a powerful resource of human

achievement in the arts, not just in the obvious terms of patronage, but also in terms of specific inspiration, constraining the style and exercise of the artistic imagination in particular directions. To take just one example, why is it that one never finds an attempt in Chinese art at a realistic representation — re-presentation — of a scene in nature? 'Never' is perhaps too strong a word. When the Italian missionary priest, Castigleone, became a court painter in China in the eighteenth century, he took the name of Nan Shih-Lin, and he began to produce Western-style paintings, which reproduced the scene as exactly and realistically as his skill allowed. In particular, therefore, he introduced Western rules of perspective and shadow. Apart from him, very few trees in Chinese paintings throw shadows on the ground. As Chiang Yee once observed (*The Chinese Eye*, London, Methuen, 1935, p. 57), 'For a while his innovation was all the rage; but the real connoisseur remained aloof'.

He remained aloof because Chinese art does not attempt to be realistic in a Western sense of imitation. In *another* sense of imitation, Chinese art *is* realistic; but then we have to ask, 'whose reality?' It is at this point that we can see the specific point of religious inspiration. Tao-chi was one of the greatest painters of the late seventeenth century, and he certainly immersed himself in nature, but what he sought to express was nature as a consequence of the interaction between 'heaven and Earth' — 'heaven' being, not the place of attainment after death, as it might be in Christianity or Islam, but, rather, T'ien, the source, the unproduced Producer of appearance and order:

> T'ien has such powers that it can alter the soul of a landscape: the Earth has such authority that it can keep in motion the breath and the pulse of a landscape. And I? I have this *i-hua*, this 'one single line' upon which I can string the forms and the spirit of a landscape.
>
> *Hua-yu-lu* 8.

This famous 'one line of the brush' is the connection between heaven and Earth, with the painter as the mediator between the two. This is the reality that Chinese art represents. It is utterly different from the 'mimesis', or 'imitation', that has been an aim of so much Western art — as Castigleone found out. Yet, when Auerbach wrote the book *Mimesis* (1946), it was as part of a massive programme to show, not how successfully painters anticipated photography (that is mere *trompe l'oeil*), but, rather, how vital was the contribution of religion — in this case, of Christianity — as inspiration to the special forms of Western art and literature. It was from Christianity and from the story of Christ in the Gospels that the West derived its emphasis on the transcendence of the trivial, on the sacralized significance of the most ordinary lives and events. Consider George Eliot, in *Adam Bede*, on old women scraping carrots, in contrast to an angel with 'a floating violet robe'. Even if one sees many in the nineteenth century as secularizing the story — for example, those ultra-realists, Zola, Balzac and Flaubert — nevertheless, they were still deriving from that specific religious inspiration the sense that great events are made up of ordinary lives (Félicité and her parrot are on a par with John the Baptist and Julien in Flaubert's *Trois Contes*).

14

Religions, Genes, and Culture

The relation of religions to art is but one illustration of the paradox of religious urgency, that religions are such bad news because they are such good news. The specific relation of religion to human creativity, constraining art, as it does, into radically different styles and outcomes, is one example of the reason why religions matter so much to those who adhere to them. They are the specific resource of so much of the most enduring human creativity; and the products of this creativity have the power to work back into human life, inspiring and educating it into new endeavour. However, this on its own, important though it is, is not a sufficient reason to explain why the commitment to religion became so intransigent. Far more fundamental is the basic fact, established in Part I, that religions are, in origin, the earliest human cultural achievements (of which we have evidence) for the protection of gene-replication and the nurture of children. We can remain sceptical about the sociobiological story taken as a whole while, nevertheless, emphasizing the truth of its observation that social organization can be a kind of 'second skin' for the defence and enhancement of gene-replication. Each of us is already sitting inside the first skin which protects the possibility of gene-replication; and culture is the second defensive skin. But then, of course, 'culture' includes anything which enhances the protection and transmission of the developmental (including genetic) process, and which can be shared

132

communally, and passed on from one generation to another. Religions are simply the earliest cultural creations of which we have evidence. In origin, they are, precisely, the cultural systems which protect the transmission of that process, though, of course, those involved knew nothing of the genes. But that is why religions 'lock on to' such basic human necessities and preoccupations as sex and food, elaborating through myth, ritual and symbol immensely complicated systems of meaning and control. In a recent work (to take a direct example), Paige and Paige have looked at the vastly diverse rituals which surround the physiological changes associated with the human reproductive cycle. Existing theories cannot accommodate the many contradictions of each other that these rituals exhibit. In their view, the only explanation that makes sense of *all* the rituals without remainder is that they are politics by other means:

> Ritual behaviour is a bargaining strategy employed out of political self-interest when more potent tactics are unavailable. In societies that lack a strong centralised state apparatus, an independent military, and a judicial system to make binding decisions about family matters, control over woman's reproductive capacity is specified by bargains between interested parties that can never be completely enforced. Parties therefore resort to ritual to declare their intentions, assess each other's intentions, and influence and gauge public opinion. Unlike other theories, ours argues that ritual is performed for the community of observers and not for the performer of the ritual (such as the father or husband) or the person on whom the ritual is performed (such as the menarcheal, pregnant, or menstruating woman).

K. E. Paige and J. M. Paige,
The Politics of Reproductive Ritual,
Berkeley, University of California Press, 1981, p. 255.

Of course, this has been contested, but it is quoted because it is a succinct reminder that religious ritual is *so* closely associated with the reproductive cycle that the case can be made, and made with some plausibility. Even so, the clear

and obvious fact that religions are immensely successful
systems for the protection of gene-replication and the
nurture of children — success here being measured in
straightforward evolutionary terms of survival and replication — does not explain why it should be specifically
religious systems that have worked so well. Why do we
need the word 'religious'? It is necessary, therefore, to add
the obvious, that the viability of these otherwise mere cultural systems has been sustained because they are the
context in which humans have made even more dramatic
discoveries, about the possibilities of their own nature
(from ecstasy to enlightenment), about the nature of the
cosmos as the bearer of meaning, about value and its exercise, and, therefore, ultimately, also about the reality and
nature of God — although, in the latter case, it seemed to
them a case much more of being discovered *by* God than of
discovering her or him. Yet, this realization of God remains
one of the most astonishing facts in the whole human
enterprise. Our ancestors came to a sense of God without
any belief that this immensely demanding and rewarding
relationship would lead to any consequence for themselves
after death (this is a point I have argued at length in *The
Meanings of Death*). Contrary to what Marx and Freud and
so many others in our times have supposed, our ancestors
did not invent God as a desperate way of securing some
compensatory life with him after death. In both East and
West, the earliest recognition of God did not carry with it
any belief that it would lead to any worthwhile life with
him after death at all: the most that might survive death is
a mere shadow, the kind of elusive memory that features in
a dream. This means that the human sense of God, no
matter how naive its early symbolic and linguistic characterization may seem to us to have been (just as ours will
seem to later generations), was nevertheless achieved and
realized within the boundary and limit of this life; it was
discovered, like hate, fire, and the wheel as a fact with
which we have to deal. No doubt the qualities within those
relationships with God created their own demand of longing and of love that this relationship might be continued,

by the One from whom it came, beyond the boundary of death. In origin, though, the quality of the fact of God did not require some further justification — it was a fact of moment in its own right.

From all this, it becomes lucidly clear why religions are so dangerous. They are elaborately organized systems, extremely well-tested and adapted through time, for the coding, protection, and transmission of the most highly valued human information. Think of the areas of human interest to which reference has just been made: sex and family; food; every manifestation of creativity; the recognition of value; a kaleidoscope of consequence inside the head; death; God. Religions are the context in which all this has been grasped and given meaning, not just for two or three centuries, but for millennia. Religions, to put it briefly, protect and transmit the means to live successfully, not only in this life, but also (now) beyond this life as well. They are the context of creativity, but they are also the creation of context, in which the practice and meaning of life are secured, and in which commitment to consequence is secured; and when religions are seen to be *this*, then it becomes obvious why people would rather die than see their religion threatened or destroyed. As a Muslim woman said to me, when we were making *Worlds of Faith*:

> I will never give up my faith . . . . Whatever happens, if the worst comes to the worst, my faith cannot be snatched from me. That's a part of my body, that's something attached to my heart that only dies when I die.

But the beliefs and practices which sustain that kind of commitment do not float about in a random way. They have to be organized if they are to be transmitted from one life, or from one generation, to another. So it comes about that religions are highly systematized. They are organized into systems for the processing of information, some of it verbal, but a great deal of it, in the religious case, non-verbal, in sign and in symbol, in mudra as much as in mantra, in the choreography of ritual, in technique, in silence. The single, simple point is that historically, religions are the earliest human cultural achievement for protecting and transmitting precisely the information that has proved true and successful in binding human lives together (*religio*), and in guiding those lives from the cradle to the grave — and, eventually, beyond the grave as well. They have supplied to human lives the means of grace and the hope of glory.

Religions, boundaries and the Inquisition

But systems have boundaries, sometimes literally so (in terms of geography), but always metaphorically so. Where you have boundaries, there you have border incidents: where a religious system comes under pressure, either literally by invasion, or metaphorically by, for example, conceptual and practical erosion, as in the process of secularization, it is predictable that there will be a defensive (or sometimes offensive) conservation of the system and what it stands for. This can be seen, at the present time, from Baghdad to the Vatican, from Belfast to Amritsar. That is not a value-judgement one way or the other; it is simply a description of what is likely to happen, given the necessity for systems to *be* systems. In the Anglican/Episcopalian church in the UK (to give another example), the word 'liberal', which has an honourable history, has become a word of denigration and abuse, applied to those who are accused of eroding tradition.

Described in this relatively neutral way, and in the security of a country that has done more than most to defend freedom, this talk of boundaries and border incidents sounds, no doubt, relatively innocent. However, it is exactly this necessity for boundaries which creates religious *in*security, which, in turn, has led to the logic and practice, not only of inter-religious conflict, but also of spiritual terrorization. There is too much at stake, in this life as much as in the next, to risk what Dostoevsky called, in the episode of the Grand Inquisitor, 'that terrible gift' of freedom of conscience. People cannot be trusted (or so operators of religious systems are inclined to believe) no matter how well instructed or informed, because there is too much at stake.

For their *own* ultimate good (as well, no doubt, as for the defence of property and the security of society), people need to be told what to say, believe and do: *Veritatis Splendor*. Of course, we are so familiar with the argument of the Grand Inquisitor that such a way of boundary maintenance must seem remote and unlikely to recur. However, it remains one of the basic arguments of the Holy Office, known now as the Sacred Congregation for the Doctrine of the Faith. At the very beginning of its process, in 1979, to establish that Charles Curran was 'no longer to exercise the function of a Professor of Catholic Theology', the Sacred Congregation made this point:

> The ordinary member of the faithful, lacking expertise in a particular question, could not prudently trust himself to human wisdom or theological opinion in making a decision, in the face of the authentic teaching of those who 'by divine institution . . . have succeeded to the place of the apostles as shepherds of the Church . . .'.

Curran, in contrast, was maintaining that where a matter *de fide et moribus* (concerning faith and morals) has not yet been defined (and the processes of definition are, obviously, an extremely clear example of a system operating for the control of information), then teaching on that matter 'does not enjoy the guarantee of infallibility'. In the process of discerning the mind of Christ, dissent may be for 'the ultimate good of the Church'. Thus, Curran agrees with Avery Dulles, in *The Resilient Church*:

> Provided that they speak with evident loyalty and respect for authority, dissenters should not be silenced . . . . Experience has shown that in many cases those who dissent from Church teaching in one generation are preparing the official teachings of the Church in the future . . . . The Church, like civil society, should cherish its 'loyal opposition' as a precious asset.

However, to those responsible for maintaining boundaries and operating systems in which, let us remember, information is being processed that is of far greater value, to those who believe it, than any other human information, such people as Curran and Dulles are guilty of a kind of eternal genocide — they are putting the eternal life of the whole human race in jeopardy. That is why Marcel Lefebvre could give a very different estimate of the Inquisition and its necessity. In his *Open Letter to Confused Catholics* he wrote:

> It is the current fashion to reject all forms of constraint and to bemoan its influence at certain periods of history. Pope John Paul II, deferring to this fad, deplored the Inquisition during his visit to Spain. But it is only the excesses of the Inquisition that are remembered. What is forgotten is that the Church, in creating the Holy Office (Sanctum Officium Inquisitionis), was fulfilling its duty in protecting souls, and proceeded against those who were trying to falsify the Faith and thus endangering the eternal salvation of everyone. The Inquisition came to the help of heretics themselves, just as one goes to the help of persons who jump into the water to end their lives.

We, in contrast, may reckon that there is a difference between, on the one hand, jumping into the water to rescue someone and, on the other, jumping into the water, interrogating the unfortunate in order to find out whether he still holds the erroneous opinion that led him to jump into the water in the first place, and then, if he does, pushing him under until he drowns. Therefore, we are likely to conclude that it is a distraction to give the Inquisition as an example of the dangers of spiritual terrorization, particularly through the opinion of Lefebvre, who was expelled from the Church (though not, incidentally, for that opinion). Nevertheless, as Ronald Knox asked the question in 1926 (Introduction to A. L. Maycock, *The Inquisition from its Establishment to the Great Schism*, London, Constable, p. xv):

> Granted that we can condone the behaviour of the Inquisitors in the past, considering the circumstances of their time, what would the attitude of the Catholic Church be towards persecution if it were, nowadays, in a position to persecute? . . . Do Catholics only admit the principles of religious toleration when they are themselves the sufferers?

He answered his own question forthrightly:

> The danger that the Catholic Church would, if it gained
> ascendancy, employ torture again in judicial interrogations
> is no greater than the danger that Mr Baldwin [the then
> Prime Minister of the UK] should employ such methods
> against the Communists.

Less than fifty years later, the UK Government was taken
before the European Court of Human Rights for using
exactly such methods of torture, not against Communists,
but against suspected Irish terrorists. The case was
brought by the Republic of Ireland in 1972, alleging torture
in the use of sensory deprivation and interrogation techniques by the security forces against fourteen internees
in 1971. The UK was found guilty of torture by the
Commission, though not guilty by the Court. However, the
Court did find the UK guilty of inhuman and degrading
treatment, contrary to Article 3 of the Convention. If a secular and democratic government can revert so rapidly, it
certainly cannot be taken for granted that a strong religious system like Vatican Catholicism will not revert also.
Indeed, under the headline, 'Protestant Myth is Blamed for
the Inquisition's Bad Name', a Jesuit was reported to have
argued in 1993, in *Civilta Cattolica*, that the Inquisition,
despite Protestant propaganda to the contrary, was not
that bad. Apart from 'the first twenty years of holocausts'
under Tomas de Torquemada, they executed 'fewer than
three people a year — far fewer than the secular courts' —
a somewhat disingenuous comment because, as the *New
Catholic Encyclopedia* (VII, p. 538) points out, the
Inquisition 'could not impose sanctions against obstinate
heretics, and this gave currency to the practice of surren-
dering them to secular authority' for punishment. Even so,
Father Brian van Hove pointed out why former Muslims
and Jews deserved punishment in any case: 'Many Moors
in Spain who had been baptised Christians were generating
heresies, while the Jews, immensely powerful in the 15th
century, could force Catholic debtors, through usury, to
renounce their faith'.

Does that really make it alright? The truth is that, in the face of strong systems, no ground is secure from spiritual — or, for that matter, from political — terrorization. We, of all people, have surely learned from the events of this century that progress is neither inevitable nor irreversible. Knox immediately went on from that last sentence to say: 'Nor do I conceive that in practice the death penalty could ever be revived'. Yet, in the United States (or at least in some of the states), the death penalty is not only being revived but also put into effect.

Taking religions seriously

This brief excursion into the domain of the Inquisition has been a concentrated example of the strong nature of some (in this case one) religious systems. Not all religious systems are the same, simply by virtue of the fact that all religions must necessarily be systems. As we will see, there are many different ways of maintaining boundaries, of transmitting and protecting information, and of monitoring the appropriation of this information in the community and in individual lives. It so happens that Vatican Catholicism is an extremely *strong* system, with all that this implies for boundary maintenance. But any religious system, if it is to continue itself through time, must find *some* way of boundary maintenance, or perish. If this seems possible, if the destruction or erosion of a religious system (or some part of it) seems possible to those who belong to it, then the imperatives of defence or of offence come into play, and, at this point, we are no longer speaking impersonally of abstract systems but of people — people who would rather die than abandon their faith.

Does it matter? Why not let people die for their faith? The blood of the martyrs is the seed of all religions, not just of the Church. But I have tried to indicate already why none of us can be complacent if we are to have any hope of bequeathing an inhabitable planet to our grandchildren. We are, most of us, well aware of the urgent demands of ecology and the environment; I have been trying to indicate a corresponding urgency in understanding religious commitment and its organization. In terms of response, I have made some practical suggestions, particularly in relation to existing disputes and conflicts, in the book *Licensed Insanities*, so it would be redundant to repeat them here. However, I would summarize the quintessential prerequisite of every response in the phrase, 'Take the religions seriously'. Never regard them as some kind of eccentric hobby that a few people take up who have not yet entered the Age of Reason. To marginalize religion is to take it off the political agenda and to decode it, for example, as fanaticism. This has been particularly obvious in the two major political systems which were dominant in the world after the Second World War. Thus, in what was the USSR, it could be recognized that religions, according to Marx, have value for people (being, in Marxist analysis, the heart of a heartless world and the genuine sigh of the oppressed creature), but that they impede the realization of our true happiness, and they must, if this analysis is correct, fade away as the dictatorship of the proletariat establishes the authentic conditions of human flourishing.

In the USA, conversely, religions were recognized, within the very process of establishing a new constitutional and political system, as having done, not valuable things, but extremely bad things to people, whenever they became associated or identified with authority and power. It was indeed accepted that religious belief, as a private and individual matter, might do much to improve the style and tone of a community or nation — hence the First Amendment: 'Congress shall make no law respecting an establishment of religion, or prohibiting the free exercise thereof'. However, because so many of the Founding Fathers had either personal experience of institutionalized religious violence or had memories of it in their own family history, John Adams was by no means alone in being, to use his own word, 'terrified' of 'the frightful engines of ecclesiastical councils, of diabolical malice and Calvinistical nature'. A consequence of this Jeffersonian 'wall of separation between Church and State' is that it is almost an act of treason to embrace, in political and economic analyses, the fact that religion is not thus separated from society elsewhere. Jefferson put it this way in his letter to the Danbury Baptist Association in 1802:

> Believing with you that religion is a matter which lies solely between man and his God, that he owes account to none other for his faith and his worship, that the legislative powers of government reach actions only, and not opinions, I contemplate with sovereign reverence that act of the whole American people which declared that their legislature should 'make no law respecting an establishment of religion, or prohibiting the free exercise thereof', thus building a wall of separation between Church and State.

However, religion in the world which most people inhabit either is the State or is so closely identified with the State that it is a constant constraint in political judgement. This is true even of a country like India, which was established specifically and deliberately as a secular State after Independence.

Thus, in the case of both the major powers in the world, there was a built-in and necessary defect in analysis — necessary, because in each case, it is derived from basic and non-negotiable commitments which are themselves ideological. Both systems were capable of producing and using highly qualified experts in the history, languages, and culture of peoples who happen also to be religious — and this remains spectacularly true of the United States — but they seemed rarely, if ever, to take religion seriously; and it is certainly hard to believe, looking at the consequences in American foreign policy, that there has been a Secretary of State (or expert adviser) who has seriously believed that other people seriously believe their beliefs.

That may seem to be a harsh judgement. Let me, therefore, give a simple example. In 1983, a conference was held in Toronto, surveying the hitherto abortive attempts to secure peace in the Middle East. The papers of the Conference were published under the title, *Peace-making in the Middle East: Problems and prospects*. The papers are divided into two parts, the first being 'The view from the inside', and the second 'The view from the outside'. In the contributions from the inside, the religious involvement in the problems is mentioned repeatedly — on average, at least once a page. In the papers from the outside — one of which reviews 'Peacemaking in the Reagan Administration' and another of which reviews 'The Soviet Union and a Middle East Peace Settlement' — religion is mentioned once and once only. It occurs in a list of four problems for the USSR: 'Fourth, since 1967 and particularly since the 1973 Arab–Israel war, Islam has been resurgent throughout the Arab world, and the USSR, identified in the Arab world with atheism, has been hampered as a result.' It is hard to believe that if anyone, from the President down, had had any more serious perception of religion than that Jews have votes in New York and Palestinians do not, there would not have been at least one mention of religion in these surveys of the process.

The point, then, is simple and clear. Religions, however else they may be described, are necessarily bounded systems for the protection, coding, control and transmission of information. While they may coexist peacefully, and even on occasion creatively in relation to each other, the potential for conflict is always latent and often manifest. If you wish to predict future conflicts, take a map of the world, and draw onto it the boundaries of religious systems or subsystems — even where they are entangled in a particular area or nation state. The potential for conflict lies along those lines. Whether such conflict breaks out depends on whether a threat is perceived internally to the continuity of any of those communities.

Religions, systems and subsystems

The conditions of body-culture coevolution have begun to make it clear why those who belong to religious systems are profoundly protective of them. The systems in which they live and move and have their being are *so* important that people are prepared to protect them against the outsider or against each other — and to do so, if necessary, with great ferocity. Wars of Religion are not simply a European phenomenon. The differences between the cultural information systems of religions are not matters of life and death; they are matters of life and Life. Religions, as we have seen in outline, are systems for the coding, protection, endorsement and transmission of information (non-verbal as well as verbal), which has proved successful in sustaining human life and communities. They are systems that have been tested not just for a few centuries, but for millennia, and their endurance is the demonstration of their success — success at the most basic level being measured in straightforward terms of gene-replication and the nurture of children and, thus, of survival.

There is much more to be said about the meaning of religious success than this — not least for the theoretical reasons established in Part I, that independent discoveries have been incorporated in religious culture of a prodigious kind. However, at the most basic level, the perspective of body-culture coevolution is correct, that religions are the earliest cultural achievements of which we have evidence, which secure the conditions of human continuity: success equals succession.

To accomplish this, religions have developed an extremely diverse range of strategies, by way of social organization, structures of authority and kinship, role-designation, controls of behaviour, processing of food, transmission of skills, and so on. There has consequently been an extremely high bias in religions in favour of the family as the major unit of transmission. On this basis, these highly stable systems have been the context in which people have been set free to make discoveries of a seemingly unending kind; and these are discoveries which have been tested for support or discouragement within the procedures of each system. Thus, even when discoveries have led to radical change, they have still been tested within the system. Among the discoveries are those that make these systems, not just cultural, but specifically religious — principally because they assign value of a transcendent and eventually absolute kind to both the sources and the goals of being human, and of the cosmos itself.

Religions thus set goals and values, and they map them on to cosmologies that locate people within a larger story, embracing the personal narrative of their lives. The point of religious cosmologies, cosmogonies, and cosmographies was clearly not to anticipate what we would regard as a naturally scientific account of the origin and nature of the universe. In fact, it is extremely rare for religions to offer a single cosmogony in the way in which a scientific account might aim to give a single, critically realistic account of the origin of the universe (e.g., Big Bang v. Steady State). Religious accounts do give accounts of both origin and nature, but principally in order to display the cosmos as an arena of opportunity. That is why religions make use of many cosmogonies at once, without making much attempt to reconcile the contradictions between them. There are at least six different types of creation narrative in the Jewish Bible (Old Testament), and many more than that in the Hindu scriptures (see my 'Cosmology, Religion and Society', *Zygon*, XXV, 1990, pp. 7–23). Religious cosmologies are more concerned to contextualize human life, reinforcing the goals and values that are set within any particular religion.

However, the protection and transmission of all this requires boundaries. Translated into life, this means that the continuing availability of this inherited wisdom requires the conditions of its own protection and transmission to be met. The boundaries (which we will look at in more detail shortly) may be literal in terms of territory, either small-scale, as usually in village religion, or on a larger scale, as one can see in the case of the Promised Land, or of India (see further p. 170); but in any case there will always be metaphorical boundaries. They secure the definition of who belongs and who does not; they set the conditions of adherence (of how one belongs); and they relate the religious system to the surrounding environment in diverse ways, and, eventually, to the cosmos itself, however the cosmos is conceived.

What undoubtedly complicates the analysis (and certainly the relation of religions to each other and to the outside world) is that no extensive religion (i.e., claiming adherents beyond the scope of a village or small community) is a single

system. Any religion beyond the local is a network of subsystems, sometimes in cooperation, sometimes in contest
and conflict with each other. Thus, any single religion will
contain a spectrum of strategies for continuity and survival
(and, in some cases, for expansion), ranging from the inclusive to the exclusive (see further pp. 174ff.). No religion is a
single system, and the subsystems may be in conflict with
each other.

This can be seen even in the loosest of all religious
systems, that which is called in the West 'Hinduism'. It is
well known that 'there is no such "ism" as "Hinduism"'. The
word is a nineteenth-century imposition on a vast array of
different religious beliefs and practices — so much so that
people are inclined to talk now not of Hindu religion, but of
Hindu religions. When I made the BBC series, 'What Do
Hindus Believe?', I was told repeatedly by Hindus that
there are beliefs among them (for example, between
Advaita and Bhakti) which are so logically incompatible with
each other that they cannot both be true, and are certainly
irreconcilable as ultimate goals. For example, an Advaitin,
relying on such texts as *Mundaka Upanishad* 3.1.3, insists
that the knower of Brahman becomes Brahman, since that
which alone is, without qualification, underlies all appearance — somatic exploration simply uncovers the truth that
what a person is, behind the ephemera of superficial
appearance, *is* necessarily Brahman: 'you are Brahman', tat
tvam asi — 'That thou art' — is one of the *mahavakyas*, the
great sayings of the Upanishads. Others, though, argue
that such texts imply not identity, but equality — in which
the self retains its individuality and enjoys the blissful
states (*vibhutis*) of Brahman, not *tadatmya* but *sa-
dharmya*. Beyond this, Bhakti (devotion) maintains that
the nature of this relatedness implies that the ultimate
source of all appearance must be understood as God, not as
the impersonal producer of all appearance *including* God.
Thus, the final union is one not of identity, but of continuing relatedness to the object of one's devotion.

However, even when there are radical divisions between
subsystems like this, there would still be a sense of

belonging to an overall and larger system. Hindus are perfectly well aware that they are not Muslims or Sikhs and, from the outside, it is not difficult to specify the constituent characteristics which enable the distinctions to be made — for example, varna and jati (division of labour and caste), karma and samsara (law-like consequences of behaviour and rebirth), Veda and Vedanta (ritual and philosophy). As always with constituent characteristics, it is not the case that *all* claimants to belonging must exhibit *all* the characteristics; and determining how many, so to speak, are necessary to legitimate the claim to adherence is a constant cause of disruption and schism in the religious case. There will always be 'grey areas' (often disputed areas) on the boundaries.

Thus, Jains and Buddhists originated (at least in part) as protestant schisms from prevailing Indian religion in their day. They took much with them, but they dissented irreconcilably at certain key points which seemed (to those from whom they dissented) necessary conditions. Both, for example, objected passionately (albeit on different grounds) to animal sacrifice which, in Vedic religion, sustains the whole cosmos. From their own point of view, they have become separate religions (or philosophies, if this terminology is preferred in order to stress the radical nature of the dissent), yet Hindus continue to regard each of them as *nastika darśana*, a maladroit interpretation of the common ground. In other words, Hindus recognize the boundary, but operate it differently. Thus, Article 25 of the Indian Constitution states quite clearly that wherever the terms 'Hindu' and 'Hinduism' are used, they are to be taken as including Jains, Buddhists, and Sikhs.

So, even in the case of the vast array that is called 'Hinduism' — where there is no single hierarchy, no creed, no single founding figure commanding allegiance — the metaphorical sense of boundary still obtains. If pressed, a Hindu might refer to the system as *sanatana dharma*, everlasting dharma. 'Dharma' is a word with many meanings, but roughly it can be regarded as something like 'appropriateness'. The Hindu way as *sanatana dharma* can then be

regarded as the map of how to live appropriately in order to
attain the goals set within the system. With a generosity
often admired in the world of inter-religious encounter,
where so much has been embittered and contested, Hindus
allow that one might live outside the boundary of dharma
and still make progress toward the ultimate goals. Yet,
even so, a threat to the continuity of dharma itself will still
evoke defensive anger. Gandhi was assassinated by devout
Hindus who believed that Gandhi, by his actions (especially
in the support he was giving to the embryonic Pakistan),
had excommunicated himself from the Hindu community.
The metaphorical boundary still obtains, even in the case
of that aggregation which is called Hinduism.

And — to repeat the point — where you have boundaries, there you have border incidents. Where people in
religious systems perceive a threat to the boundary
(metaphorical though it may be), at least some of them will
predictably become defensive or offensive. Even religions
committed to non-violence will, in some circumstances,
allow that there is a necessary or just war. Thus, to give an
example, let us return to the Jains. Observant Jains sweep
the path before them and strain the water they drink, lest
they hurt the jiva, the 'soul reality', in any living thing.
Indeed, since jiva is entangled in plants as much as in animals or humans, the ultimate religious act is *sallekhana*,
voluntary death. It is not suicide; it is controlled abstention
from all food in a condition of concentrated meditation (in
which hunger makes no demand) until death happens to
occur. Thus ahimsa, non-violence, is taken to the highest
extreme of virtue among Jains. It is better to die than to
cause pain to the jiva within an animal or plant. Yet
Jinasena's famous *Adipurana* contains clear instructions
on the ways in which Jain kings should behave, and this
certainly includes warfare in defence of the Jain community and of Jain doctrine and teaching, and it includes
defence against the Brahminical religion of the Hindus.

As religions are distanced (conceptually, if not always
geographically) from each other, they justify war in different ways (and in ways that often exemplify exactly this

tension between exclusive and inclusive voices. Thus, in a system with a belief in rebirth, it may be the duty (for example, the dharma) of warriors or soldiers to engage in warfare on behalf of others as, at this stage in their progress, it may lead them on towards heaven and better rebirth. It is the classic argument of the Hindu epic, *Mahabharata*: 'Samjaya said: ". . . Your father Devavrata, who knew all the precise details of dharma (*sarvadhar-maviśesajñah*) summoned the kings and said to them: 'This is the wide entrance to heaven, noble ones, which is open before you: enter through it to pass into the worlds of ´Sakra and Brahma . . . . It is against dharma for a Kṣatriya [one of the class of warriors] to die of illness at home: his eternal dharma (*sanatana dharma*) is to die on the battle-field'"' (*Bhagavadgita* 17.7, 11). It is, of course, one of the main arguments that Krishna uses to persuade Arjuna to fight, in the book that is most precious to most Hindus, the Gita.

Among Sikhs, the appeal to dharma is equally important to justify what is therefore called *dharam yudh*, 'a war of righteousness'. Guru Nanak (the first Guru) insisted that tyranny and injustice must be resisted, and Guru Amar Das (third Guru) told those who were Kṣatriyas that it was their dharma to establish a protective fence of justice around the community. Under the tenth Guru, Guru Gobind Singh, rules of warfare were drawn up, establishing five conditions for a justifiable war: it must be an action of the last resort; the motives must be pure; it must not be for gaining territory; the soldiers must be committed Sikhs who will, therefore, observe the rules; and minimum force must be used.

Among Christians and Muslims, considerations of dharma and rebirth obviously do not apply, but war is still justified — and with considerable attention to detail in the conditions of jihad and of the 'just war'. *Jihad fi sabil Allah*, striving in the cause of God, may be 'warfare' against any evil or temptation (the greater jihad); the lesser jihad is defensive warfare to protect a Muslim country or community, and it can *only* be defensive (for a summary of the conditions, see A. R. I. Doi, *Shariah: The Islamic Law*, London, Ta Ha Publishers, 1984). According to Muhammad, 'In avenging injuries inflicted on us, do not harm non-belligerents in their homes, spare the weakness of women, do not injure infants at the breast, nor those who are sick. Do not destroy the houses of those who offer no resistance, and do not destroy their means of subsistence, neither their fruit trees, nor their palms.'

Christian considerations of the just war go back to the *iustum bellum* of the Roman empire and to the practice of warfare as commanded in what Christians call, the Old Testament. However, the latter was so (apparently) corrected by the New Testament commands of love and forgiveness that it has always seemed to some Christians that *no* war can be just, and that pacifism is an obligation. However, they have been in a minority. Theories of both *ius ad bellum* and *ius in bellum* were developed. For the former, there must be a just cause (to regain something wrongfully taken, to punish evil, or in defence against planned or actual aggression); a right authority initiating the war; a right intention on the part of those engaged; a proportional use of force; a recognition that war is entered into as a last resort, with the purpose of peace and with a reasonable hope of success. For the latter, there must be proportionality of means and discrimination of objects.

The inescapable truth is that the protection of well-tested and highly valued information requires boundaries, both literal and metaphorical. Provided the boundaries are reasonably secure, religions can live peacefully with each other, not just in adjacent territories, but often entangled with each other in the same territory. It has often been pointed out that, until very recently, Jews were, for long periods, a great deal safer in Muslim countries of the Near East than they were in Europe. However, the possibility of conflict is always latent, and may become expressed if insecurity or threat is perceived, even if it arises from a totally extraneous source.

15

Somatic Exploration and Exegesis

It is the necessity for boundaries as a condition of continuity and transmission which makes religions potentially so dangerous. Religious systems require bounded conditions for their own continuity, whether we are observing a street in Calcutta or the splendours of the Vatican in Rome. How religious people handle this requirement varies, not only between religions, but within them, as we shall see. A preliminary question is whether one might use the universals of *human* continuity to transcend the boundaries and to establish a religious ecumenism. Might one at least diminish the sense of isolation between religions by using the underlying insight of theories of body-culture coevolution (that there are near-universals of human nature that underlie cultural variations) in order to establish a common ground between religions? We might then be able to establish the claim (often made) that religions are simply variations on the human theme, perhaps even different paths to the same goal or different languages about the same ultimate realities.

There is, of course, an important and immediate truth that underlies this quest for a more peaceful religious ecumenism. Whatever religions claim to have discovered — in terms of gods and ghosts, heavens and hells, trickster and trance, or whatever — all these discoveries have been made and then subsequently appropriated by those who live in

151

bodies; and these bodies, marginally differentiated now by
such things as skin pigmentation, have virtually everything
in common at the level of the developmental process that
brings them into being. Organs can be transplanted across
the boundaries of religions, although some religions would
object to this being done. This means that the discoveries of
religion have been, in the first place, discoveries about, and
discoveries made on the basis of, the human body. Religions
are a consequence of what we may call, for the sake of
brevity, 'somatic exploration' — what exactly is it that this
body is capable of doing, of experiencing, of being, of becoming? What kind of environment does it inhabit? Religions
exploit behaviours and possibilities which are inherent in
the human body, and develop them in ways which bind the
body (*religio*) to the meaning and value of the system in
which its life is embedded. That some are driven to break
the bond by the sheer power of the religious achievement in
their own case does not affect the underlying common
ground.

We have already looked briefly at one particular example
of what this means, the example of dance (pp. 64–5). As we
saw, ethologists describe what they call 'choreographed
behaviours' among animals, birds, and insects serving
many functions — sexual display, establishing hierarchies,
marking territories, threatening rivals, and the like. Many
human dance behaviours serve exactly these purposes. And,
however much the human appropriation of dance then goes
on to transcend the ethological base, there is no question
that dance is sufficiently embedded in the human brain
(and, thus, sufficiently 'prepared for' in human brains by
the developmental process that produces all humans) for
it to be able to serve these and all the other developed
purposes. Indeed, Wagner, in pursuit of the absolute and
perfect art-form, had no doubt that dance lay at the root:
'The most original of arts was that of dancing: its peculiar
essence is rhythm, and this has developed into music.'

However, rhythm — equally universally — does strange
things inside the human head. Rhythm, especially when it

is emphasized by drumming, excludes other stimuli, and many people under its influence fall into trance states. This is a discovery, shareable and repeatable, made within the boundary of the body; it is a consequence of somatic exploration. Not surprisingly, therefore, dance is deeply embedded, not just in the brain, but in religion as well — spectacularly in the examples of the whirling dervishes, of the achievement of *bittul hayesh* among the Jewish Hasidim, of the Ghost Dance, of the Japanese Noh theatre, and, consummately, of the Natya ´Shastra tradition of India, epitomized in ´Siva as Nataraja, the famous Lord of the Dance.

Dance serves such purposes and delivers such satisfactions in the human case (given the sort of brains and bodies that we have) that dance was an inevitable discovery in the process of somatic exploration. However, it is not a simple 'happening'; it is interpreted, and the interpretations cannot be divorced from the event: they are, so to speak, 'what it is'. Humans, by the means of language on the basis of consciousness, engage also in 'somatic exegesis' — in interpretation of the discoveries that they make.

It is the exegesis, just as much as the event, which gets taken up and protected in religious systems, and which thereby gets extended into other lives. It is because religions are based on the near-universal structure of the human soma (body) that they can establish connection from one life to another, and from one generation to another. One of the major consequences of religion has been the eventual achievement, not just of the extended family, but of the extended tribe, binding (*religio*) disparate people into a common enterprise — with all the evolutionary advantages that this allows. As a consequence of religion, it is never a case just simply of 'Me and My Girl' — which was reviewed, incidentally, in the *New York Times,* in 1986, under the heading, 'A Pas de Deux of Flirting and Fun'. The reviewer described it as, 'A virtually uninterrupted duet of seduction, an exquisitely choreographed collage of tickling, kneeling, lounging, smoking, reading, sliding, leaping, posing, massaging, pushing, shaking, pulling, bouncing, tugging, stretching, crawling, limping, yanking, waving — not to mention singing as well'.

Most of us know how much fun a *pas de deux* of that kind can be. It was the achievement of religion to extend the exercise of life beyond the pair, beyond the family, beyond even the kinship group, into the shared values and practices of much larger communities — the ultimate being Islam, which envisages the whole human community as belonging together in a single *'umma* (people), or Paul, drawing in the entire cosmos as well in the body of Christ (*Colossians* 1.15–20). These are visions of unity that should make the relation of religions into, not so much a *pas de deux*, as an entire *corps de ballet* — and of much more than flirting and fun.

However, because religions are the stable contexts of continuing somatic exegesis, religions become increasingly divided from each other. The reason is obvious. The exegeses (interpretations in the plural) not only vary from each other in themselves, they have, through time, come to set different priorities, different evaluations, different goals for the enterprise of being human.

If, then, we are seeking a more peaceful coexistence of religions on the basis that they are variations on a common human theme, the question 'Do the differences of somatic exegesis between them make a difference?' becomes inevitable. Or might we instead be able to track back and rediscover the somatic aptitudes which underlie the very divided religious exegeses of their meaning? At first sight, that seems an attractive path to follow:

> Hath not a Jew eyes? hath not a Jew hands, organs, dimensions, sense, affections, passions? fed with the same food, hurt with the same weapons, subject to the same diseases, healed by the same means, warmed and cooled by the same winter and summer, as a Christian is? If you prick us, do we not bleed? If you tickle us, do we not laugh? If you poison us, do we not die? And if you wrong us, shall we not revenge?
>
> *The Merchant of Venice*, 3. 1. 63.

To undertake a quest for a more peaceful and cooperative human community, based on the somatic universals that make possible both exploration and exegesis, seems an obvious step to take; and it is a procedure that already underlies many of the ecumenical and irenic meetings of religions. It has the added advantage that, as already indicated (pp. 62f.), we can be critically realistic in our accounts of what we experience and, yet, at the same time, accept that our descriptive languages about virtually everything are usually provisional, corrigible, approximate, and frequently (at least from a later point of view) wrong. However, as we saw, because of the great reliability of many of our languages, we still have to ask the question, are they wrong about something? Is there whatever there is in reality which sets a constraint and limit on appropriate (as opposed to private or eccentric) language, even though we can never know exhaustively the whole of what anything may be?

If we take this line, then religions could be understood to be expressing provisional and approximate accounts of what we all have in common — namely, the bounded competence of the human body and of the operational environments (pp. 42–6) in which it is set. In other words, they could be understood to be approximate accounts (which, for this reason can *appear* to be in conflict with each other, though in fact the conflict is only superficial) of what is, nevertheless, the common human ground of a developmentally processed and energy-demanding body. On this account, religions would have a common subject-matter which might then transcend the details of difference between them.

Do differences make a difference?
Inversive and extraversive systems

But that approach does not deal, in itself, with the question of whether or not these differences do, in fact, make a difference. To this we can say immediately that it would be extremely odd if they do not, precisely because religions are a consequence of somatic exploration in which genuine

discoveries have been made and then endorsed — many of
them for long periods of time. To argue that the differences
which have resulted from this are semantic rather than
substantial is to trivialize the seriousness of the religious
enterprise.

We can see this by means of a single illustration. In
terms of the possibilities and competence of the human
body, which of two directions of exploration is to be given
priority? Is it to be its competence to form relationships
beyond itself or is it to be its competence to arrive at profound experience and truth within itself? It is trivial and
misleading to answer 'Both — why do we need to give priority in practice to one or the other?' The truth is that *in
practice* we cannot do both at once, or even in sequence, at
the levels of seriousness that religions have achieved after
millennia of exploration and discovery. Take the point as
it was put by Henry Thoreau, when he said that there is
no object in going round the world to count the cats in
Zanzibar (*Walden*, Chapter 18):

> Is it the source of the Nile, or the Niger, or the Mississippi,
> or a North-West Passage around this continent, that we
> would find? Be rather the Mungo Park, the Lewis and
> Clarke and Frobisher, of your own streams and oceans . . . .
> Nay, be a Columbus to whole new continents and worlds
> within you, opening new channels, not of trade, but of
> thought. Every man is the Lord of a realm beside which the
> earthly empire of the Czar is but a petty state, a hummock
> left by the ice. Yet some can be patriotic who have no *self*-
> respect, and sacrifice the greater to the less. They love the
> soil which makes their graves, but have no sympathy with
> the spirit which may still animate their clay.

The emphasis here is on religious exploration discovering
truth within the boundary of the body, as many religions
do. Thoreau knew that the journey is not easy: 'It is easier
to sail many thousand miles, through cold and storm and
cannibals, in a government ship with five hundred men
and boys to assist one, than it is to explore the private sea,
the Atlantic and Pacific ocean of one's own being alone.' So,
religions that give priority to inward exploration offer

initial support and guidance — through guide, guru, or roshi — but, in the end, the attainment lies beyond the company of the guide.

Buddhism as an inversive system

Thus, in Buddha-dharma or Buddha-sasana (the religious system known in the West as Buddhism), there is no permanence in the external world; there is no subsistent or persistent reality unaffected by *anicca*, impermanence, transience. There is not even an enduring or eternal self or soul — no atman, as the Hindus were beginning to maintain, that goes on being reborn from one life to another until it obtains its *mokṣa*, or release. In Buddha-dharma there is only the process of constant cause and effect, with nothing permanent to be found within it. When Gautama, who was, through his enlightenment, to become the Buddha, set out on the exploration into truth, he tried virtually everything that was on offer in religion and philosophy at that time. Pragmatically and experimentally, he reached the point where he entered into profound meditation, and passed through the four dhyanas/jhanas, leading to 'a state of profound stillness and peace, in which the mind rests with unshakeable one-pointedness and equanimity, and breathing has calmed to the point of stopping; the mind has a radiant purity, . . . depths having been uncovered and made manifest at the surface level; it is said to be very "workable" and "adaptable" like refined gold, which can be used to make all manner of precious and wonderful things' (P. Harvey, *An Introduction to Buddhism*, Cambridge University Press, 1990, pp. 250ff.). However, as Harvey immediately goes on to say, this was simply the basis of further exploration and discovery: 'It is thus an ideal take-off point for various further developments.' And as the Buddhist exploration of the nature of impermanence continued, so it came to be realized that if there is nothing more permanent or real than anything else, then, in truth, everything is of the same nature. Whether it appears as a tree, or a house, or a body, everything is of the same

nature, namely, the nature of having no permanent characteristics. In this way, the majestic philosopher, Nagarjuna,
arrived at the insight of *śunyata*, of everything sharing the
same nature of being equally devoid of permanent characteristics.

Then, though, the puzzle arose: if *śunyata* is true of all
appearance, so that all things are equally empty of permanent characteristics, then it would seem that the nature of
all things is to have no permanent nature; but they have at
least this nature in common, namely, the nature of having
no nature. Consequently, the continuing somatic exploration
and exegesis which issued in the emergence of Mahayana
Buddhism not only explored the interior nature of the soma
on this basis, but also incorporated the consequences in
new formulations of what they must mean, eventually
drawing the conclusion that the 'nature of having no
nature' is precisely the Buddha-nature, and that the
Buddha-nature is, equally, the nature of every appearance.
'Religion' is life lived on the basis of these conclusions,
appropriating them as truth for oneself — indeed, appropriating them as the truth that one is. When Banzan was
walking through a market, he overheard a conversation
between a butcher and a customer: 'Give me the best piece
of meat you have', said the customer. 'Everything in my
shop is the best', replied the butcher. 'You cannot find here
any piece of meat that is not the best.' When he heard
those words, Banzan immediately became enlightened: the
words precipitated him into the realization (wholly, and not
just intellectually) that everything is equally of the same
nature, which is to have no separate nature.

However, if everything, no matter what its outward,
transitory appearance may be, is of the same 'nature that
has no nature', and if all things, wisely understood, *are* the
Buddha-nature, then they even came to the conclusion that
nirvana, the goal — that condition of perfect equilibrium
where the no-nature is dynamic but no longer interacting
with any other appearance — is not a goal outside the
realm of appearance. Nirvana is not some thing or some
place additional to the Buddha-nature: it is as much the

Buddha-nature as every aspect of every appearance in the phenomenal worlds; and if this is turned inside out, then every appearance already is nirvana if its true nature is properly seen and understood. Why, then, go outside yourself to find what is equally and indistinguishably already within? You already are what Dogen called 'the serene mind of Nirvana' — you have only to realize what is already the truth.

It follows that the task of a guru or roshi is not ultimately to *teach* anything; it is to help people (and the means are many) to become what they already are. On the way to this ultimate realization, there may be many surprising discoveries. For example, in Zen, a person may attain kensho, or the lesser, or even the greater, satori: these are well-known, well-marked experiential consequences of this particular enterprise of somatic exploration. They are undertaken, not (as Thoreau supposed) alone, at least in the first instance, but, rather, at least initially, in a network of achieved and inherited experience, protected and transmitted in a religious system.

As always, this system, the Buddha-dharma, is not monolithic or absolute: there is contest and conflict within it. Thus, Theravadins (those who follow the teachings of the Elders) might not regard the developments of Mahayana as representing the authentic teaching of the Buddha; within Mahayana, not all would regard the emphasis on meditation in Zen as wholly balanced; and within Zen, there is a marked division between those who seek sudden enlightenment on the one hand, and those on the other who believe that enlightenment is a gradual unfolding.

Yet, the many forms of Buddhism are identifiably within the same boundary. The constituent characteristics that they hold sufficiently in common mean that it is not inappropriate to call them *all* 'Buddhist'. Certainly, within Buddha-dharma, the emphasis is on *inward* exploration. It is what we may call, for the sake of brevity, an 'inversive system'. Another example is the way of the Jains. It does not mean that Buddhists and Jains are unconcerned with external relationships. Far from it. Buddhists, for example, know that right conduct in the world (*sila*) is a *sine qua non* as the foundation of a true life; and, among Jains, the great vows (*mahavrata*) of the ascetic, which are directed towards a renunciation of the world, are carried on the foundation of the twelve vows of the layman (*anuvrata*, *gunavrata* and *śikṣavrata*), which are all concerned with helping the layman regulate his relationships in his environment.

Scholasticism as an extraversive system

'Extraversive systems', in contrast, are those which are also based on millennia of somatic exploration and exegesis, but in which value is given to the body's relatedness to external environments. Once again, it is a matter of emphasis. There are no extraversive systems (for example, Christianity or Islam) that do not attend to the interior states which arise from faith or iman. The 'Interior Castle' of St Teresa of Avila, for example, is there to be explored and defended: 'The door by which we can enter into this castle is prayer. It is absurd to think that we can enter Heaven without first entering into our own souls, without first getting to know ourselves.' Even so, the highest perfection remains the aligning of our interior disposition with the will of one external to ourselves: 'Wherein lies the highest perfection? It is clear that it does not lie in interior delights, but in the conformity of our will to the will of God .... We forget our own pleasure in order to please him who loves us so much.'

This emphasis on the exploration of external environments leads, in extraversive systems, to the inference (often an abductive inference) that there is some degree of reality (perhaps, indeed, unqualified reality) in what is discovered 'out there'. A classic example can be found in the three sentences which characterize the epistemological achievement of medieval scholasticism: the first, *nihil in intellectu quod non fuit prius in sensu*, there is nothing in mind or intellect that was not first in a sense (i.e., the external world enters us through our senses, and the mind builds its worlds on the basis of those impressions); the second, *mens convertit se ad phantasmata omnia*, the mind turns or conforms itself towards those sensory images (i.e., the worlds we build are limited in relation to truth by whatever it is in reality that has given rise to these sensory impressions); and, therefore, third, *mens quodadmodo fit omnia non entitative sed intentionaliter*, (the mind can, in a particular way, become all things, not by being what they are, but by stretching out into them).

'Stretching out' is an extraversive quest for truth. The contrast can be seen in the amended way in which a Buddhist can read these sentences with approval, especially if he belongs to the Cittamatra, or Mind Only, school. Cittamatra maintains that mind or consciousness is all that there is, a flow of appearances with no underlying substantial reality. So, where the scholastics believed that mind, as it turns to the appearance of an external world, is right to draw the inference that there must be sufficiently what there is in reality in order for the images (the phantasmata) to have the stable appearance that they do, Cittamatra believed that this is the fatal error that binds us to ignorance and reappearance. They would, therefore, have rewritten that last sentence — 'the mind, in a particular way, creates all things, not in actuality, but by its ignorant craving for substance in a world of process'. Consequently, the goal must be to overcome ignorance by right views and correct perception, to be led by the mind only and to rest in an undifferentiated field of pure consciousness, which is the anticipation of nirvana.

In this way, Cittamatra is a religious or philosophical system which sets goals, priorities and values, and designates the boundaries within which these can be attempted and attained. They are very different from the goals and priorities set within medieval scholasticism. It may indeed be the case that

'Passing soon and little worth
Are the things which please on earth'

as a Buddhist would agree. But for a Christian or a Muslim,

they have at least this abiding merit, not only that they require the inference of a sufficient ground for their presenting themselves to the senses in the way that they do (a sufficient substance, to use the scholastic language), but also that their transience points beyond itself as requiring a sufficient ontological ground and source to cause and maintain their being — in other words, God.

Buddhists do not deny that there are appearances in consciousness which are appropriately labelled 'God' or 'gods': Buddhism is an extremely theistic religion (as I have illustrated in *The Religious Imagination and the Sense of God*) — in quantity, even more so than Hinduism, since Buddhism absorbed Hindu deities (on its own terms of understanding what deities are), and then added many more wherever it went in the world. Those 'terms of understanding', though, reduced theistic appearances to the same status as that of any appearance, that is, lacking any permanent reality in themselves. The gods are simply forms of appearance, the flowing together of the aggregates of appearance in the form of gods as opposed to, say, the form of humans. God is certainly not *extra*-cosmic — outside the process of appearance in a universe of this kind as its unproduced Producer.

In contrast, an extraversive system equally explores what occurs, what is possible and what is experienced within the body, but it also considers what must, at least inferentially, be the case in the external environment for such somatic consequence to take the form it does. Consider, as an example, a passage near the opening of Aquinas' *Summa Contra Gentiles*:

> The way of making truth known is not always the same. For as the Philosopher has very well said, *it belongs to an educated man to seek such certitude in each thing as the nature of that thing allows* . . . . But since such is the case, we must first show what way is open to us in order that we may make known the truth which is our object.
>
> There is a twofold mode of truth in what we profess about God. Some truths about God exceed all the ability of the human reason. Such is the truth that God is triune. But

there are some truths which the natural reason itself is able to reach. Such are that God exists, that He is one, and the like. In fact, such truths about God have been proved demonstratively by the philosophers, guided by the natural light of reason.

That there are truths about God which totally surpass man's ability appears with the greatest evidence. Since, indeed, the principle of all knowledge which the reason perceives about any being is the understanding of the very substance of that being (for according to Aristotle *what a thing is* is the principle of demonstration), it follows that the way in which we know the substance of a thing determines the way in which we know what belongs to it. Hence, if the human intellect comprehends the substance of some thing, *e.g.*, that of a stone or of a triangle, no intelligible characteristic belonging to that thing surpasses the grasp of the human reason. But this is not what happens to us in relation to God. For the human intellect is not able to reach a comprehension of the divine substance through its own natural power. For according to its manner of knowing in the present life, the intellect depends on the sense for the origin of knowledge; and so those things which do not fall under the senses cannot be grasped by the human intellect except in so far as the knowledge of them is gathered from sensible things. Now sensible things cannot lead the human intellect to the point of seeing in them the nature of the divine substance; for sensible things are effects which fall short of the power of their cause. Yet, beginning with sensible things, our intellect is led to the point of knowing about God that He exists, and other such characteristics which must be attributed to the First Principle. There are, consequently, some intelligible truths about God which are open to the human reason; but there are others which absolutely surpass its power.

This is an argument which leaves this particular extraversive system of Christian argument poised for the exercise of analogy which points from its *own* being to the source of *all* being, the unproduced Producer of all that is, who *is*, even when there are no bodies here at all. Somatic exploration and exegesis have led to truth outside the body; and

the extraversive systems which culminate in God are clearly
going to set God as priority and goal, and certainly as the
source of value.

Culture and language

So, we come back to the question, 'Do the differences make
a difference?' Do these particular differences between
inversive and extraversive systems make any serious difference or might they, for example, be regarded as alternative
languages about that which is ultimately true? After all,
both God and nirvana are beyond description, so might we
not simply regard them as approximate languages for the
same ultimate goal?

The answer, clearly, is 'No'. The one affirms and the
other denies that the condition of relationship with that
which is external to one's own centre of experience is *the*
ontological truth with which we have to deal — so much so
that, on the extraversive side, the claim is made, both by
Hindus and Christians, that interrelatedness must necessarily belong within the very nature of God, in the Trinity
in Christianity and the Trimurti among Hindus. We have
already seen that there is division among Hindus concerning
the nature of what is ultimately real (p. 146), but this simply reinforces the point that differences make a difference:
we cannot slide over these distinctions as though they
arise from nothing more than the limitations of language.
Inversive and extraversive systems set different goals and
encourage different procedures on the basis of endorsing or
of transcending relationship with that which is external to
oneself. It is not surprising that Advaita and Bhakti are
themselves contrasted as inversive and extraversive — a
reminder that both can be found within a single overarching system.

Thus, even if we can, as seems evident, establish some
basic somatic universals, it does not follow that we can
decode religions as variations on a common somatic theme,
because the many centuries of religious exploration of the

body and its possibilities have achieved startlingly different results. Nor can these achievements be translated directly from one religion to another because they are embedded in contexts of exegesis and technique which belong inextricably to them — though, of course, particular texts or techniques and the like can certainly be transferred between religions, as increasingly they are. However, even then, they are transferred into a new meaning and value system which makes them other than they were; that is why attempts to reconcile religions by uniting what they have in common end up as new religions, as, for example, in the case of the Bahais and (though the example is not exact) of the Sikhs.

In a comparable way, this is where the debate in anthropology about the nature of human nature has led. As we have seen, there is no 'innocent abroad', no 'pure person' who simply puts on the clothes of the culture or religion into which she or he is born. It is, rather, the culture or religion (or absence of religion) which characterizes the sort of person that we are. However, as culture and religion both arise from somatic exploration, they have picked out and endorsed a wide diversity of different possibilities of being human, and, in their exegeses, they have created what are, in effect, different bodies and different worlds.

Thus, culture and language are not casual clothes thrown over the bare body that we all have in common. Religious and cultural interpretations of the body carry with them such different styles, goals and strategies that they cannot be synonyms for each other. Consider the dress of an American footballer and Margot Fonteyn. Yes, they *both* cover the human body, but they each relate to different possibilities of that body, which require contextually committed training, and which result, not just in different experience, but even in different muscular development. In one sense, they are interchangeable — a person might move from being a footballer to a ballet dancer — but, in fact, that person will have moved from one world to another, and the objectives, the procedures and the rewards in each case are very different. As long ago as 1929, Edward Sapir argued that 'the worlds in which different societies live are distinct worlds, not merely the same world with different labels attached'. This argument was countered by the suggestion that, in some cultures, there happens to be an unimportant deficit, so that, if the necessity or opportunity had been there, the requisite skills would have been forthcoming. The claim, in other words, was that there is a kind of latent human nature, not all potentialities of which are deployed in any particular culture. Thus, there was neither need nor opportunity in earlier societies to develop the understanding of the world which issued in the natural sciences; earlier societies *could* have done so, but had no *need* to do so. In fact, what we now realize is that if and when they do so, they enter a new world and radically alter the old. For a culture with an emphasis on inversive exploration, the extraversive exploration of environments is not a valued priority; and it is unsurprising that the natural sciences as we know them emerged from specifically Muslim and Christian roots. So, when Shweder and Bourne asked the question in culture theory, 'Does the concept of a person vary cross-culturally?' (in R. A. Shweder and R. A. LeVine, eds, *Culture Theory: Essays on mind, self and emotion*, Cambridge University Press, 1984), they answered:

> In this essay we have tried to show that different peoples not only adopt distinct world views, but that these world views have a decisive influence on cognitive functioning. People around the world do not all think alike. Nor are the differences in thought that do exist necessarily to be explained by reference to differences or 'deficits' in cognitive processing skills, intellectual motivation, available information, or linguistic resources. It is well known in cognitive science that what one thinks about can be decisive for how one thinks . . . . What's not yet fully appreciated is that the relationship between what one thinks about (e.g., other people) and how one thinks (e.g., 'contexts and cases') may be *mediated* by the world premise to which one is committed and by the metaphors by which one lives.
>
> p. 195.

The world views which are religions undoubtedly lead to this consequence. It is an arrogance of the worst kind to suppose that the differences between them are a matter of semantics, and that religions are really 'talking about the same things' in different languages. That approach empties of all significance the many different discoveries that religions have made and endorsed about the bodies we live in and the world we inhabit. Differences *do* make a difference. But the vital point then follows: the fact that differences are serious and substantial does not, in itself, determine what should be done about them. Diversity does not dictate damnation for the outsider 'just like that'. The relations between systems are not determined by the observation that systems have boundaries. The issue still remains of how boundary relations might best be monitored and maintained.

16

Religious Constraints and Boundaries

The argument so far has been that religions are derived from somatic exploration and exegesis, which has made religions the context of memorable and treasured discoveries, not least the discovery of God. However, the securing of these discoveries and of the information and technique required to reiterate and extend them, has meant, inevitably, that religions have emerged as systems for the coding, protection and transmission of all this accumulating information. To use the language and analysis of systems does not imply that everyone within a system will think and act in the same way (though there will usually be high rewards, in this life or the next, for conformity). A religious system is always an aggregation, sometimes a coalition, of subsystems, with many ways of relating the parts to the whole; and, again, individuals or smaller groups of people appropriate what is on offer in a system in highly personal, often idiosyncratic, ways, so there can be real dissonance between official and personal (or folk, or local, or implicit, or private) religion, which creates constant and recurrent anxiety for the controllers or operators in authority in religious systems.

So, there may be conflict or contest within a system, and many competing ways of appropriating whatever the resources and values are in a particular system. If the strain

168

gets too great, then there may well be a schism and, indeed, new religions. However, in general, the point about a religious system or subsystem, where behaviours are concerned, is that it sets constraints of appropriateness over individual and social behaviour. We have already encountered the word 'constraint' (p. 106), and there it was pointed out that although the word constraint sounds negative and restricting, it is, in fact, extremely liberating and positive. As we saw, it is a basic insight of biology that the more degrees of constraint there are over an organism, the greater are the degrees of freedom available to it. A stone is constrained by extremely little beyond the laws of motion; you and I are constrained in extremely elaborate ways and, for this reason, you can do more than lie about in a field all day.

Where human behaviour is concerned, the truth of this is absolutely vital — constraint is the condition of freedom. If you accept constraint on your initial freedom and spend hours at the piano, you will end up with the far greater freedom of playing the piano and composing your own music. If you accept constraint on your theoretically unlimited degrees of freedom and place yourself under a roshi in a Zen monastery, you will attain far greater degrees of freedom at the end of the process.

Constraint, then, is the condition of freedom. Religions, therefore, impose (or try to impose) constraint in order that goals of far greater freedom can be attained — not only proximate goals of wisdom, but also ultimate goals such as God, the Garden, Sukhavati, Nirvana — or the equally great freedom of being able to act entirely for others and not with reference to one's own advantage. The loss of self is, in all religions, the greatest gain (hence the lists on pp. 125f.).

The problem which religions pose in the world is that the constraints of religious information have to be coded and protected if they are to be transmitted from one life, or from one generation, to another. This coding and protection require the organization of systems, and systems require boundaries, and boundaries carry with them a necessary degree of isolation, which may, on occasion, require defence.

The boundaries religions establish and maintain may, of course, be of many different kinds. They may be literal: for example, the Indian law code, *Manusmriti*, defines India as the boundary within which alone the proper observance of dharma is possible:

> The land between the two sacred rivers Sarasvatī and Dṛṣadvatī, this land created by divine powers is the Brahmāvarta. The customs prevailing in this country, passed on from generation to generation, that is called the right behaviour (*sadācāra*). From a Brahmin born and raised in this country, all men should learn their ways. The country where the black antelope naturally moves about is the one that is fit for sacrifice — beyond is that of the *mlecchas* [the barbarians, the unclean!] A twiceborn [viz., a Brahmin, a Kṣatriya, a Vaiśya] should resort to this country and dwell in it; a 'Sūdra, however, may for the sake of gaining his livelihood live anywhere.
>
> 2.17–24.

However, far more often, the boundaries are metaphorical. They are the conditions of continuing community and of adherence to it. These metaphorical boundaries can be established and maintained in many different ways — for example, by ritual, creed, birth, behaviours, subscription, law, compulsion, consent. The boundaries can be extremely strong, resulting in high-definition systems, or they can be almost self-destructively weak, resulting in low-definition systems. A high-definition system, like Vatican Catholicism, usually regards a low-definition system, like Anglicanism, with an incomprehension amounting to contempt. Yet, both represent ways in which the coevolution of the developmental process and culture is translated into the somatic explorations of religion. Either is viable, and they result in very different styles of life, which are subject to different kinds of threat and vulnerability.

Strong and weak boundary maintenance

In order to see this contrast more clearly, we can take the example of two different groups: at one extreme, the Amish, at the other, the Bauls.

The Mennonites emerged as a movement of radical reformation in the sixteenth century, already tightly bounded
by rules of appropriate behaviour, and marked out in
particular by Anabaptism, the baptism, or rebaptism if
necessary, of believers who understand the commitment
they are making. From the Mennonites, there emerged an
even more strictly defined group under the leadership of
Jacob Ammann, many of whom migrated to North America,
where they formed the people known as the Amish.

The boundary definition in this case is literally obvious:
the Old Order Amish separate themselves from the society
around them by retaining the dress and customs of that
early period of their origin — beards and broad-brimmed
hats for men, bonnets and aprons for women, no cars, no
electricity in their homes. They separate themselves, as far
as possible, from surrounding society, having their own
schools, refusing military service, and not accepting Social
Security benefits from the State. Their discipline includes
the avoidance of those who are under the ban of excommu-
nication, even if they are within the family, and, as there is
no missionary activity and marriage is always within the
Amish community, the growth or maintenance of their
numbers depends on the large size of their families.

Contrast that kind of strong boundary maintenance with
the Bauls of Bengal. Here, again, we are dealing with a
subsystem of a subsystem. The Bauls are derived, in part,
from the Sahajiya, who, in turn, were derived from the
Buddhist siddhas who emphasized the central importance
of *sahaja* (hence the name, Sahajiya). *Sahaja* is the
absolute truth, which can be found within the body. So,
this is an example of an inversive system. *Sahaja* is the
essence of everything, the unmoving and ineffable state,
which is far beyond *vikalpa*, or thought construction. It is,
therefore, *maha sukha*, the great bliss, and, as such, it
became a synonym for nirvana. In that logical move (which
we encountered on p. 158), *Hevajra Tantra* states: 'The
whole world is of the nature of *sahaja*, because *sahaja* is
the essential nature (*svarupa*) of everything. This essential
nature is nirvana for those who possess *citta* [i.e., who see
things rightly, p. 161].'

When the tide of Buddhism went out of India, the Sahajiyas (i.e., those whose lives are devoted to realizing sahaja within) did not go with them. They merged with Hindus, but they did not become identical with them. In other words, they maintained the boundaries of their own identity, adherence, and continuity, and they did so, in part, by identifying the bhakti and tantric exegesis of sexual union with the manifestation of *sahaja*. In making this the central religious act they appeared to be recapitulating the divine union of Radha and Krishna in a straightforward way, although, in fact, the tantric techniques were exemplifying a different inversive claim.

Out of this tradition emerged the Bauls. 'Baul' is Bengali for 'mad', so these people were, as Novalis called Spinoza, 'god-intoxicated men'. They have their boundaries of adherence and continuity, but, in contrast to the Amish, the boundaries are extremely weak. They draw on any resource which reinforces their central preoccupation with God discovered within (lending himself to behaviours that lie far beyond the ordinary conventions) — not just the Buddhist and Hindu traditions of their origins, but also the Sant tradition of North India and the Sufis of Islam. They have no creed, no code of practice, no doctrinal scheme — they simply share a common belief that God is most truly and accessibly to be found within a person as 'the caged bird', known also as 'the Man of my heart'. How do you find and release the caged bird? By following 'the contrary path' (*ulta sadhana*), which leads away from the world and its conventions to the divine within the body. They wear tattered clothes, indicating their rejection of worldly values; they ignore distinctions of caste; and although they may be found in Vaishnava temples and attending festivals, they are not there to find God outside themselves: 'What need do we have of temples when our bodies are temples where the Spirit abides?' The boundaries are so loose that they pay little attention to the history or tradition of their 'order' as they mistrust reliance on precedents and traditions. They have gurus to initiate beginners in the way, but they are inclined to call them śunya (cf. p. 158).

Here is a religious system which is at the opposite end of the spectrum from the Amish, yet both of them *agree* in rejecting the world around them. The difference is that whereas the Amish give clear markers of what this rejection must involve, the Bauls regard any such markers as fatal distractions from the main task of finding God within. Even so, they have a tradition and means of transmission, however relaxed the boundaries are.

17

Fundamentalism and Inclusiveness

Differences, therefore, make a difference, and boundaries protect and continue them. This very basic fact, though, does not determine how people in religious systems should operate the necessary and inevitable boundary control and maintenance. At an extreme, a threat to the boundaries of a religious system (or subsystem) will lead to what is known loosely as fundamentalism.

'Fundamentalism' is obviously a word with many different uses and applications. In general, it is a description of those who defend or celebrate what they believe to be the fundamental truths and practices of a religion. As a word, therefore, it has been applied to this attitude of people and movements in all religions — for example, to the resurgence of conservative Islam; to ha-Haredim among the Jews (those who literally tremble at God's word; see *Isaiah* 66.5); to the Rashtriya Svayamsevak Sangh among the Hindus; to the Dhammakaya movement of Thai Buddhism; to the Confucian revival in East Asia; to political nostalgia in Japan. What is it that unites these vastly different human enterprises?

It was to answer this question that the Fundamentalism Project was set up in 1991 in Chicago, by the American Academy of Arts and Sciences, and its reports have begun to appear. The key point in common is that those who belong to these movements are reacting against modernity, but (to quote the first report, *Fundamentalisms Observed*, M. E. Marty and R. S. Appleby, eds, Chicago University Press, 1991), they 'no longer perceive themselves as reeling under the corrosive effects of secular life: on the contrary, they perceive themselves as fighting back, and doing so rather successfully' (p. ix).

So, fighting is the key. According to the Report, they fight in five ways: they fight *back* ('resisting some challenge or threat to their core identity'); they fight *for* (for 'their conceptions of what ought to go on in matters of life and health'); they fight *with* (selectively with, not the whole of 'a pure past', but 'those features which will best reinforce their identity, keep their movement together, build defences around its boundaries, and keep others at some distance'); they fight *against* (not so much the outsider as the insider 'who would be moderate, would negotiate with modernity, would adapt the movement'); they fight *under* (mainly under God, but in a minority of non-theistic cases, under some transcendent and commanding reference).

Fundamentalism is thus generated in religions — and always will be — by the very process of time and change, as these threaten the stability of existing boundaries. Fundamentalists are people who turn up at the negotiating table in order to make the point that nothing on the table is negotiable. This certainly does not sound like good news for the creation of peaceful human community. At the opposite extreme, though, there are those who operate and maintain boundaries in an utterly different style, which indicates that operating a religious boundary does not carry with it an automatic aggression against the boundaries of other religious systems.

We can, again, take two examples of this. The Jains, as we have seen, are an example of an inversive system, which addresses itself to the problem of how to release the jiva (soul reality) from the dense accumulations of karma in which it is entangled. However, it is not necessary to become a Jain in order to make at least some progress in this direction. Already by the sixth (or perhaps eighth) century CE, Haribhadra was defeating Buddhists in debate, and yet he was also arguing that 'the ultimate truth transcending all states of worldly existence and called nirvana is essentially and necessarily one and the same, even though it may be referred to by different names' (*Yogadristisamuccaya*, 129–30).

This led Haribhadra to what we may call 'the logic of nirvana': if nirvana turns out to be nirvana, it is nirvana that nirvana turns out to be, even though you and I may have been speaking about it in approximate and rival ways. If the Earth turns out to be spherical, it is spherical that the Earth turns out to be, even though you hold that it is round and I hold that it is flat. We are both wrong, but at least we are approximately wrong about something. We may argue, as Haribhadra did, and try to convince each other; and, in the end, one position may be more approximately right than the other. But it will still be about a spherical Earth that flat Earthers and round Earthers happen to be arguing. On the basis of this 'logic of nirvana', Haribhadra concluded that 'It is impossible for thoughtful people to quarrel over the way in which one expresses one's loyalty to this truth' (p. 132). It follows also, in his view, that anyone who points the way (however approximately) to what is truly the case must be honoured — whether a god, a guru, a brahman, or an ascetic. So, Jains maintain their boundaries, but they do not feel an aggressive need to extend the boundaries, or compel others to come inside.

Nor is this attitude confined to religions whose anthropology allows for many millions of rebirths (so that, eventually one might be led to birth as a Jain). As a second example, Orthodox Jews (an extraversive system) pay much attention to maintaining the boundaries of religion and to living appropriately within them. The opening words of *Pirqe Aboth*, The Sayings of the Fathers, are a kind of epitome of this policy, at the root of the rabbinic tradition: 'Be deliberate in judgement, raise up many pupils and place a fence (*syag*) around Torah'. Most Jews regard the *literal* boundary of the Promised Land as a necessary condition of the completion of God's purpose in the messianic kingdom (though not all Jews regard the present contest for land as having much, if any, connection with this because, if it happened, it would have to be a consequence of the direct initiative of God). However, in any case, Orthodox Jews do not seek to bring others into the same boundary, or to contest the boundaries of others, as a condition of gaining a share in the messianic kingdom. In fact, exactly the opposite: *hasidei 'umot ha-'olam* (the righteous gentiles who keep the very general commands entrusted to Noah) will have a share in the 'Olam ha-Ba (the world to come) when the Messiah arrives. What would be the point of burdening themselves with the 613 commands and prohibitions of Torah? Jews have a specific vocation to undertake these, not on behalf of themselves and their own advantage, but on behalf of the whole world. There is no need to bring others inside the fence (even though there was a period, about the time when Jesus was alive, when Judaism was a highly successful missionary religion).

Styles of relationship

So, it is not a function of boundary maintenance that religions must be aggressive in relation to each other or to the non-religious outsider. On the other hand, aggression, predictably, will occur in the case of any religious system in which the conditions of attainment (whether of proximate or of ultimate goals) can only be discerned and observed within the boundary of that particular system, because in this case, the system (and living within it) is the necessary condition of human good or of human flourishing (cf. p. 110), however this is defined.

Take the example of Islam. Muhammad (and all Muslims after him) pursued the logic of nirvana but applied it to God: if Allah (that which is God) turns out to be God, then it can only be God that God turns out to be. All claims to serve and worship God, however flawed and approximate they may be, can only be claims in relation to that which is truly God. Thus, Jews and Christians are clearly flawed and defective (from a Muslim point of view, using the Qur'an as the measure and control) in what they say about

God, not least because they argue with each other and contest the nature of God. However, it is about God that they
offer their flawed accounts. It is the Qur'an alone (albeit
supported by *ayat*, or indications, in nature) which makes
available a true understanding of God and of what a
human response to God should be. So, the world of religion
can be measured according to al-Furqan, the criterion, of
the Qur'an; in so far as some peoples have retained a sem-
blance of the revelation entrusted to them, even though
they have corrupted it, they can be regarded as ahl al-Kitab,
a people of the Book, and they are related positively to
Islam in terms of legal status (they can, for example, retain
their religious beliefs and practices if they are under
Muslim jurisdiction). However, those who flagrantly insult
the nature of God (by, for example, continuing to worship
God under the form of idols) must be contested, if this is
feasible.

On this basis, Islam divides the world, as Caesar divided
Gaul, into three parts. The first is dar al-Islam, the house,
or domain of Islam; the second is dar al-harb, the domain of
war, wherever there is opposition to God or to the bearer of
God's service on Earth (i.e., Islam); and the third is dar as-
Sulh, the domain of treaty, those areas not yet subject to
Muslim rule with which treaty relations have been made
(akin, therefore, to dar al-aman, the domain of safety, the
kind of treaty of recognition and protection which Muhammad made with the Christian community at Najran). In the
end, all people must necessarily belong to a single 'umma
(p. 154), a single world community, because all people come
equally and indistinguishably from Allah who alone creates
them. So, by one means or another, it is the responsibility
of Islam to recover the intention of God in forming all people once more into the single *'umma* under God. It does not
mean (at least theoretically) that *all* people must follow the
observances of Islam. Rather, if they are among the ahl
al-Kitab, they can continue to worship Allah in their own
way, but it *is* Allah they are worshipping.

Thus, the boundary of Islam is potentially the entire
human race. On its way to the realization of this goal,

different strategies are allowed and, in the meantime, existing Islam is (or should be) the manifestation of what must eventually be the entire human case.

In a way, these three houses of Islam have a kind of counterpart in the three ways in which Christians have summarized the possible styles in which the Christian relation to non-Christian religions might be understood, though, in this case, we are dealing with three strategies, and they illustrate how sharply opinions can differ on such matters, even within a single religion. The three strategies are usually described as exclusivist, inclusivist, and pluralist.

The exclusivist position holds that it is 'necessary for salvation' to come within the boundary of the Christian community, which is the consequence of Christ's redemptive act — and this may even include other so-called Christians (i.e., those who are not located in the true definition of this particular community). Thus, when the Bull *Unam Sanctam* of 1302 declared that 'there is one holy, catholic and apostolic Church, outside of which there is neither salvation nor remission of sins', and that 'it is altogether necessary to salvation for every human creature to be subject to the Roman pontiff', it mentions specifically 'the Greeks' (i.e., the Greek Orthodox). Thus, *a fortiori*, those in other religions must be in equally great peril (unless protected by invincible ignorance). This view — extra ecclesiam nulla salus, outside the Church no salvation — has been repeated consistently. It was affirmed by Pius IX in the allocution, *Singulari Quadam* ('It must, of course, be held as a matter of faith that outside the apostolic Roman Church no one can be saved'), and by Councils (e.g., Fourth Lateran, Florence), and the First Vatican Council was only prevented from stating this position as a dogma by the outbreak of the Franco-Prussian War. It is a position profoundly modified by the Second Vatican Council, but the threat which that Council posed to the stability of the traditional boundaries has led to an increasing reassertion of the exclusivist position. Thus, Cardinal Basil Hume and many other Roman Catholics greeted the transfer of Anglicans to the

Roman Catholic Church in response to the Synod decision
to allow women to be ordained (see Part III) as the first
hoped-for sign of the conversion of England.

It is this view, which puts the Christian (or, in this case,
the Roman Catholic Church) at the centre of the universe
of faiths, that John Hick believes he has overthrown in his
'Copernican revolution'. In this, he demands that *God*
should be put at the centre, not one particular religion or
Church, so that religions can then be regarded as different
planets circling the same centre. This is a pluralist view,
which accepts all religions as ways of salvation (though
they might not use that particular word), and sees all religions as pointing, in their different ways and different
languages, to the one God, for, by the logic of Nirvana (p.
176), if it is God at all who is dimly perceived in so many
different ways in different religions, it must be *God* who is
so perceived: 'The varying divine personalities worshipped
in their respective religious traditions, and likewise the
varying non-personal forms in which God is known in yet
other religious traditions, are all alike divine phenomena
formed by the impact of God upon the plurality of human
consciousness' (J. Hick, 'Towards a Philosophy of Religious
Pluralism', *N.Z.S.T.R.*, XXII, 1980, p. 142).

Unhappily, the Copernican revolution is logically inco-
herent, historically false, and descriptively inadequate —
for reasons which have, in part, been argued in this book
and also in my article, 'Christianity and Non-Christian
Religions: A Neo-Darwinian Revolution?', in A. Sharma,
ed., *God, Truth and Reality*, London, Macmillan, 1993).

Mediating between these two positions (the exclusivist
and the pluralist) is the inclusivist. Inclusivism accepts
other religions as ways of salvation, but regards the effecting of that salvation as having been achieved objectively
in the work of God in Christ. Thus, an inclusivist acknow-
ledges, with gratitude, the fact of this redemptive act and
hangs on to this as being the objectively central truth of
God with which we have to deal — or with which, rather,
he has chosen to deal with us. In this case, the adherents of
other religions are included in a positive relation to God

and Christ, even though Christ is hidden from them; and
their divergent ways (cleansed no doubt from all offence)
might then be regarded as having much of value to contribute to the human response to God — much as the magi
(as seven missionary bishops put it in a seminal work in
1907) brought their own treasures to the infant Christ.
This is, somewhat, the approach of the second Vatican
Council or, more colourfully, of Rene Cutforth's Anglican
uncle in Bombay:

> He was an Anglican clergyman about 80 years old who
> closely resembled a tortoise. He'd been in India for 60 years,
> completely immersed in Sanskrit roots and the translation
> of bits of the New Testament into Marathi. He was also
> wildly eccentric to the point, some people said, of insanity
> . . . . In the end, he left India under a cloud.
>
> He'd been in charge of a little church at Miri on the
> Bombay side, and what with the Sanskrit and the Marathi
> and the heat and living all by himself miles away from any
> other English people, he'd begun to fashion the Anglican
> Service more to his own way of thinking, and when some
> ecclesiastic called in there at the time Charles was nearly
> 80, he found a very odd state of affairs. There was a cross
> on the altar, but there were also Shiva and the Elephant
> God, and others of the Hindu Pantheon. Most of the service
> consisted of dancing and drumming with elaborate chants
> in Sanskrit all written to the tune of 'Champagne Charlie is
> me name'. Nowadays he'd be regarded as an ecumenical
> pioneer, but in those days they simply shunted him back to
> England with the suggestion that he was off his rocker.

Differentialism

What lies at the heart of this debate about the relation of
religions to each other (in this last case, of Christianity to
other religions) is the evaluation of difference: *do* the
differences make a difference in ultimate terms? A fourth
solution, which allows the differences to be carried to their
ultimate conclusion, might therefore be called 'differentialism'. This does not attempt to coerce the (approximately and

corrigibly expressed) accounts of ultimacy in each religion into the claim of any one of them (since more than one may be correct), still less does it allow an indefinable category of 'ultimacy' to coerce all religions into being approximate accounts of the same thing, namely, whatever ultimately turns out to be the case, because it is logically (and theologically) possible that *much* will turn out to be the case. Differences lie deeper than semantics. The consequences of inversive and extraversive systems (in, say, nirvana on the one hand, or the communion of saints on the other, where relatedness and interaction are endorsed) cannot be made the same on the basis of semantic inadequacy. However, as ultimate states, it makes little sense to try to rank them in order of value. Both may be attainable and attained.

From a theistic point of view, this is unsurprising — it is coherent with any understanding of creation which allows (indeed, delights in) diversity, that the possible goals should be diverse but equally, so to speak, ultimate. After all, religions have envisaged a goal of hell, and some religions have regarded this goal as being ultimate. There may be arguments about the virtue of that, but it at least makes the possibility of ultimate diversity unsurprising. But perhaps more to the point, the claim of differentialism is that there may be equal outcomes of value which cannot be translated into each other. The urgency of argument will still remain. Buddhists have lives and arguments which point to the virtue of nirvana, and these lives and arguments will be, to some, persuasive. Conversely, Christians manifestly will try to persuade others of what is on offer through the death of Christ. But, perhaps after all 'where your treasure is, there will your heart be also'; and perhaps, therefore, God (from the Christian point of view) endorses the outcomes which his creatures, created in freedom (though no doubt burdened by karma or sin) have attained, both with his help and beyond his help.

This would engender an attitude which envisages argument remaining at the heart of the encounter of religions (after all, not all things are necessarily true, on any account, simply because someone says them); and religious encounter will continue to have a missionary impetus (because choices are seen to be even more searchingly important). However, because the differentiated nature of the ultimate condition is accepted, the consequences of grace and truth in other religions can be held in wonder, respect and awe. Only then will that mutual encouragement and criticism become possible which the religious world so much needs. Then, too, the cooperation of religions in resisting evil and assisting goodness becomes an uncomplicated priority. A differentialist lives out of the truth which has set her free, but she respects the differences, even to the end, rather than regarding other religions as, at best, ways to the one salvation to which her own religion holds the key.

18

Means and Ends, Boundaries and Freedom

In all these ways, religions operate boundaries. There is nothing in the fact of boundaries themselves that dictates how they should be maintained or defended. What complicates the involvement of religions in political encounters (or in interfaith dialogue) is that there is never unanimity in a religious system — although *official* pronouncements can state exactly this, the official view (if there is one, and if there is a mechanism for articulating it).

Of critical importance, therefore, in understanding why religions can be so dangerous is the tension that can arise between official figures in a system and those who live within it. In any system, there are always those for whom the maintaining of the system becomes an end in itself, rather than being the means to an end of greater freedom. On p. 169, it was pointed out how systems impose constraints which, if internalized, lead to greater degrees of freedom (or of attainment). Because those who monitor and maintain the boundaries of a system are usually those who have authority within it, a major dissonance can arise between those who regard the conditions of continuity in maintaining the system to be an end in itself, and those for whom what is on offer in a system is appropriated as a means toward ends which transcend the system altogether — so much so that they may even turn back on the system which has given them life and change or even contradict it

184

(Jesus in the midst of Judaism or the Buddha in the midst of Brahmanical religion are only obvious and extreme examples of a recurrent dynamic in the processing of religious information). At one extreme are those for whom the defence of the system (not least against the claims or incursions of other religions) is vital if the truth which is being protected within the system is to be transmitted to other lives and other generations. At the other extreme are those for whom the appropriation of this truth into life requires a generosity in relation to other systems which manifestly are capable of producing an admirable beauty and gracefulness of life: 'By their fruits shall ye know them', and not by their philosophy, still less by their theology. God is about goodness, and goodness can easily be recognized for what it is, no matter what its origin may be — hence the almost interchangeable lists on pp. 125–6.

Yet, of course, beauty and grace do not happen by chance: they require the constraints of one system or another to make them more probable in life. And systems require boundaries; and boundaries will always, on occasion, produce border incidents. It is the same point: political or economic or religious analyses of a particular situation must take seriously the reasons for religions being such strongly bounded systems, particularly when they are involved in intransigent conflicts. Religions are bad news (when they are) because they have been such good news in human history. Quite apart from all that they have achieved in securing human continuity and the discovery of much interim truth, they point, on their own account, to the final truth of the entire human and cosmic adventure. They are not going to be abandoned lightly by those who believe.

Options and freedom

The tensions of the present time have been much exacerbated by the ideological systems which have come to dominate at least the industrialized world and, increasingly, all other parts of it as well. The conflict between religious and political systems had seemed most obviously to involve the Marxist attempts to eradicate religion. However, in fact, the far more serious threat to religions (from their own point of view) has been created as a result of a very different revolution — the political and social revolution, which has been committed to securing the maximum autonomy of individuals within the boundary of law. This is a revolution which has taken place in industrialized societies through three centuries of often bitter struggle to maximize the autonomy of individuals. In political terms, we refer to the consequences of this struggle as 'democracy', and it required rebellion against the existing form of authority — for example, against king and parliament, in which, in the case of America, even Christians participated, despite the fact that the authority of kings seemed to have Biblical warrant and command. It is a revolution — derived not least from the Reformation of the Church — which has introduced 'the Rights of Man' — and, somewhat belatedly, the Rights of Women.

However, this emphasis on the autonomy of individuals has implications far beyond the political. It is a commitment to the maximum freedom of choice for individuals and groups within the boundary of law and always under the constraint of the generation and distribution of wealth. Paradoxically, the greater the freedom, the more the law, because the boundary has to be set and understood if the exercise of freedom is to be possible.

This move in the direction of freedom, autonomy and tolerance is what I have called 'a preferential option for options' (i.e., we give maximum value and endorsement to the choices that people make in the ways they live, within the boundary of law; that is what is meant by 'the option for options'). However, it carries with it two massive threats for religions. First, it disentangles religion from politics, or Church from State, as we already observe in the American Constitution. Second, it makes religion itself optional, one choice among many; but for virtually all religions, religion is not optional: religion is the entire definition of life — *din* for Islam, *sanatana dharma* for Hindus, *shen-tao* for the Japanese, Torah for Jews, and so on.

All of this makes it obvious why, for such people as Cardinal Ratzinger, the Enlightenment was such a disaster. It began to shift responsibility *to* the individual, *away* from the authority of the Church. It leads to the privatization of morality, and this is regarded as a defect, despite the fact that, in the end, personal morality must always be privatized; it must become the personal decision and act of an individual (the privatization of morality is a cumbersome way of talking about conscience). In fact, what Church leaders who attack the privatization of morality are attempting to talk about is the making of personal decisions without reference to independent and objective authority. However, autonomy, accountability and responsibility — what the Church used to call 'conscience' — will not go away simply because the Grand Inquisitor, whether of Dostoevsky or of the present Pope, believes that people cannot cope with too much freedom: 'There is nothing more alluring to humans than this freedom of conscience, but there is nothing more tormenting, either' (*The Brothers Karamazov*, pp. 298f.). The failures of freedom are no doubt obvious all around us, but the catastrophes of dictators are even greater, whether in Church or in State.

So, despite the fact that some religions, and especially some parts of Christianity, have been major agents in effecting this revolution in the direction of freedom, the consequence has been that religions in general (or some people within religious systems) have perceived it as a threat to their own boundaries and continuity, as, indeed, in some ways, it is. The wedge that is driven between religion and modernity has virtually nothing to do with much-vaunted issues (such as 'science versus religion'); it has to do with issues of continuity and transmission, and the threat to them. There are, of course, religions or parts of religions which have attempted to relate the preferential option for options to the responsibilities of faith and practice. Ironically, the Anglican Church (see, e.g., its reports, *Believing in the Church*, and *We Believe in God*) has attempted exactly this, and has been constantly derided for doing so.

Thus, at the present time, there are many in religions who feel vulnerable and threatened, and who behave accordingly. Because religions are entangled in so many of the apparently intractable problems of the world, it is essential that those involved in trying to resolve such problems gain a far more serious sense of what religious boundaries are and of why they matter so much.

Guidelines in conflict

Where religions are involved in conflict — and supposing that the command leading to the blessing of peace matters to us — there are some elementary guidelines to bear in mind, which are all the more important if the United Nations is to continue to be involved in peace-keeping or peace-making exercises.

The first is to establish who is actually involved, and who, in the background, is offering support. There are no such people as 'Muslims', 'Christians', 'Hindus', and so on — religious life is always more detailed, specific and complicated than that, as the earlier discussion of subsystems has tried to show. However, on the other hand, if the conflict is inter-religious, those involved will often identify themselves with the entire system, and think of themselves as Muslims, Christians, Hindus, and so on. The actual relation between subsystem and system may well be decisive in suggesting appropriate action.

So, the second is to ask (and find out) how the issue in question looks from within the subsystems of the religions involved; and to bear in mind how it looks from the viewpoint of the overarching system, which may offer, at least theoretically, some controls. Thus, the IRA, despite the context and affiliations of its members, has been increasingly distanced from the Roman Catholic Church. For the outsider, there is no Archimedean ground on which to stand in order to issue superior judgements. No doubt, as outsiders, we will make our own judgements, but they will not fly nearer the sun than the birds already in the air.

The third, therefore, is to learn to argue within the logic

of the systems involved. This requires a great deal more than a knowledge of the relevant languages, although, obviously, it is a necessary condition of any conversation. It should then be possible to see what the logic of each system demands — *or forbids* — in relation to a particular issue. Logic rarely wins an argument; but it establishes what ought to be relevant to it.

The fourth is to define, from the respective points of view of those involved, what the point or purpose or cause of this particular issue is, remembering then to set it in a wider network of constraints, since it is often *there* that the true root of intransigence is to be found.

The fifth is to bear in mind that many people would rather die than abandon their faith (p. 135), and that they are, consequently, prepared to die, and carry others with them into death, in ways that seem incredible to an outsider. Differences are profound and cannot be negotiated away as semantic inadequacies. It is essential to understand how a religion arrives at non-negotiable truth (i.e., at what counts as non-negotiable truth from its own point of view) according to the limits set within this tradition on legitimate or appropriate utterance. Otherwise, all you will hear will be either the vague expressions of goodwill which bring inter-religious meetings into such disrepute; or nothing.

The sixth is to establish, in any conflict in which religions are involved, what the perceived conditions of continuity are for the participants involved: on what terms do they perceive that there is a reasonable chance that their grandchildren might grow up as Shi'a Muslims, Vaishnava Hindus, Orthodox Jews, or whatever (bearing in mind the first point above about the relation between subsystems and systems)? No one knows the future. But this is not an exercise in exact prediction. Rather, it is a way of eliciting participant perception, by asking the following question in a practical way: 'What do you think you need in order to secure the continuity of your lifeway, not just for tomorrow, but into some reasonable future?' Usually when this question is asked, the answer comes back, 'Everything'. But, at the other end of the spectrum, the Jews in the camps of

Europe required virtually nothing to retain their Jewish identity and their faith. Somewhere between the two extremes, between everything and nothing, there will be a compromise which is worth the risk; and if the word 'compromise' is an unhappy one — a good umbrella but a poor roof, as Lowell called it — then take instead Samuel Johnson's 'reciprocal concessions'.

The seventh is to apply the argument in Part I of this book: talk not of causes, talk, rather, of constraints. This removes from the arena contest about 'who caused' the conflict: in a network of constraints, responsibility is diffused and face is saved.

The eighth is to remember, in the religious case, always, at some point (preferably early on), to follow Thomas Hardy's advice and take a full look at the worst. Religions can be extremely bad news, especially for those of whom they disapprove. However, at the same time, they are the source of immense goodness; faith is constantly moving mountains a little to the right, making the possible happen and the impossible take a little less long. The aim has to be to get the goodness of a system to engage with the evils the system is endorsing, or allowing, or ignoring, or setting forward — goodness and evil, that is, on its own terms of reference. What rapidly becomes apparent is that the definitions are not actually relative, and that there is a very extensive religious consensus concerning both good and evil. Religions *can* be allies in healing the Earth. Perhaps what is needed is not so much an Amnesty International as an Uposatha International (Uposatha is the fortnightly meeting when Buddhist bhikkhus, monks, review their offences against the basic code of behaviour, the Patimokkha — the review is against their own code, since there is no neutral Archimedean point on which to stand). What religions might one day attempt is a mutual reinforcement of each other in attempting to secure the behaviours which are appropriate, or moral, or good according to their own system. For example, reference has already been made to the firm statement in the Qur'an, 'There shall be no compulsion in religion'; as we have seen, *shari'a* (Muslim law) makes specific provision for non-Muslims who are 'peoples of the Book' to practise their faith. If this does not happen, the protest against the betrayal of God and of his messenger can only effectively come from within dar al-Islam, the house of Islam. However, if other religions reinforce this protest, it can only be if they accept a comparable critique of the betrayals in their own case — betrayals, not in a generalized sense, but in the terms of appropriate conduct which lie in their own sources of constraint.

Religions are powerful resources in the enterprise of being good, generous, and just, despite all there is in their present behaviours and past histories which contradict that. Unless we find some collective means to take this 'full look at the worst', without pulling down the house all around us in the first moments of outrage, we will never reach the point where the resources of goodness and reconciliation can be mobilized together. Religions will continue to exhibit exactly what Roger Woddis wrote about, of Europe, in a poem called 'Europhoria':

> Gloria, gloria, Europhoria!
> Common faith and common goal!
> Meat and milk and wine and butter
> Make a smashing casserole!
> Let the end of all our striving
> Be the peace that love promotes,
> With our hands in perfect friendship
> Firmly round each other's throats.

PART III

The Nature of Women
and the
Authority of Men

Introduction

In 1992, the General Synod of the Church of England voted
for legislation to be passed which would enable women to
be ordained to the priesthood. The first such ordinations
took place in 1994. Other Provinces in the Anglican Communion had already begun to ordain women as priests and
to consecrate them as bishops, but the prospect of the same
happening in England evoked passionate and angry argument. Even after the first ordinations, the issue of reception
remained open (the issue, that is, of how the ministry of
women will be received). Outside the Anglican Communion,
large parts of the Church resist any move in the same
direction: among Roman Catholics, the debate is only just
beginning (and the present Pope has made a strong bid to
silence it), and among the Orthodox it has scarcely begun
at all.

This debate is deeply embedded in all that has been
argued in the first two parts of this book, because it raises
issues of change and continuity in religious systems; and it
raises them in relation to the themes of body-culture coevolution in a very direct way. The status and role of women
have been established over many thousands of years in
religious systems, in ways that are inextricably connected
with the cultural protection of gene-replication and the
nurture of children. Because religions are systems for the
protection of exactly this kind of cultural information, they
are inherently conservative (if they were *not* so conservative, they could not have endured so successfully for so

many thousands of years). When change of a more than
trivial kind is proposed in an area of this kind, the resistance will be vigorous, and will, predictably, appeal to both
nature and culture in order to indicate why the change is
illegitimate; and precisely because, as we have seen,
religious systems are so well-established for their own
protection, the arguments will also appeal to sources of
legitimacy and authority within the system itself — for
example, to revelation.

This relation of religions to body-culture coevolution can
be seen in many instances, ranging at the present time
from the treatment of animals to the evaluation of homo-
sexuality. However, a particularly clear example happens
to be the issue of the ordination of women. The purpose of
this part of the book is to exemplify this close relation
between body-culture coevolution and a particular religious
issue of change, and to examine how well arguments which
appeal to nature and culture stand up in relation to the
ground covered in the first two parts of this book.

From the outset, the point made above has to be emphasized, that religious systems are necessarily conservative.
For religious systems in general, the past is necessarily
normative (this is a key and recurrent argument in the
Roman Catholic rejection of the ordination of women in
Inter Insigniores): a role and a status for women have been
established in the past which conform to their nature. On
this view, cultural changes cannot call into question the
normative definitions of the past because such changes are
a matter of ephemeral and passing fashion. The fact that
such change might be demanded not simply by wiser or
truer insight into a particular matter, but actually by the
logic of truth within a particular system (so that such
issues would have to be considered with discrimination and
judgement), is not addressed. The possibility of change is
decoded as a subordination of religious truth to the tran-
sient concerns of the world. For many of the opponents of
the ordination of women, it is clearly a matter of the
Church giving way to the clamour of feminists. To agree to
the ordination of women would be to subordinate the

Church to the world: it would be to allow the world to dictate the agenda of action to the Church, instead of the Church making a prophetic stand against the standards of the world. Elizabeth Mills, the public relations officer of Women Against the Ordination of Women, put the argument in the following way:

> The views of Ms Furlong and other feminists are very popular . . . because they seem to tell us that the Church is just another structure which can be moulded and changed to suit the mood of the moment, thus seeming to bring God under the control of mankind.
>
> *Church Times*, supplement, 10 July, 1992, p. ii.

Elizabeth Mills is wrong. The truth is that the world has *always* set the agenda for the Church — the Latin word 'agenda' means 'the things that ought to be done'. The world set the agenda for God when he saw its distress and sin, and sent his only begotten Son into the world to redeem it. The Church derives its life and being from the Incarnation and so can scarcely expect to be isolated from time, history, providence and change. This is very far indeed from 'suiting the need of the moment'. The point is that the work of the Church is to extend this same redemptive action of God precisely into those areas of human failure and sin which the Church's attitude to women (as in the past to Jews and to slaves) so bitterly exemplifies. We forget too easily that the world, however alienated it is now from the intention of God, nevertheless remains God's world — His creation; or as the Books of Proverbs and of Wisdom put it, God's world is *Her* creation, the design and constant re-creation (recreation) of Wisdom, for which the words in Hebrew and in Greek are feminine.

However, there are clearly more serious arguments against the ordination of women than this. They rest, particularly, in the claim that the ordination of women goes against the natural order which God created, that it belongs to the natural nature of men and women that men should have authority and headship over women. Therefore, the ordination of women, setting them in authority over men, would contravene what is called technically 'a creation principle', that is, something that lies in the created order of God. It follows that culture will (or should) reflect these creation principles, so that, in culture, there will be clearly defined roles and opportunities for men and women, some of which will be exclusive.

19

Religions and the Role of Women

The foundations of this argument are evident in the points already made. Putting it once more as briefly as possible, either a human community finds a way to ensure gene-replication and the nurture of its children or the community loses out and moves towards extinction. Religions are the earliest cultural systems we know about which have created strong protections for replication and nurture, not least by controls over behaviour — hence the preoccupation of religions with sex and food (think of the sex and food laws in Judaism or in Islam).

In the past, therefore, the status of women in religions has been tied closely to the reproductive cycle, both that of humans, and also that of crops and herds. It was in and through religious systems that a necessary division of labour was eventually developed and justified — based on biology, but extended symbolically, so that women came to be responsible for the upbringing of the family and for related activities in preparation of food (both in cooking and in the fields), and with men relating to a wider environment, such as hunting, warfare, political relations.

Thus, the feminine is often celebrated in religions as the source of life and the gift of fertility. The feminine, as Mother Goddess, was the primordial focus of worship. At a time when the male contribution to reproduction was not realized, the reverence for the female as the sole source of life is unsurprising. Equally unsurprising (from a genetic point of view) is the way in which men consequently took control of the reproductive cycle. There was nothing else they could do about it. Male dominance compensated for their inferiority in the reproduction of life. However, historically, it led to the increasing suppression of the Mother Goddess, and the increasing assertion of patriarchal religion. Male control goes along with male protection. No doubt, as we have seen, religious systems also produced the context in which humans had sufficient security and confidence to make those immense discoveries (about their own nature, about the universe as the bearer of meaning and value, about God) which have made religions the source of virtually all the most enduring of human achievements. That, to say the least, has reinforced the strength of religious systems, as it still does.

Yet, still we need to remember the ways in which religions were (and more unevenly still may be) the (unconscious) expression of somatic evolutionary strategies. This is why the religious subordination of women to the authority of men is not usually one of status, since women, and their role in the family, may be very highly revered; more often, the subordination is one of control and protection. Put this together with profound fears about the dangers surrounding sexuality, and you end up with religiously sanctioned restrictions on the opportunities afforded to women to dispose of their own lives (and bodies and property) according to their own decisions, and you end up, also, with literal separations of women from men, especially in worship (for example, in synagogue or mosque or in the Roman Catholic refusal, until 1992, to have girl servers near the altar).

So, the subordination of women to men became widespread in all religions, and it did so for entirely wise evolutionary reasons, given the circumstances in which people of those times were living. To that extent, one *can* say that the subordination of women to men did lie 'in nature': it had a biogenetic base, *but not 'eternally so'* — only for as long as those life-styles were being rewarded in natural selection. Equally, it is unquestionably true that the genetic endowment which men and women receive contributes to a different experience of themselves and of the world. Men and women are, indeed, different.

However, it cannot follow from those observations that there is some natural and innate 'character of women' which never changes and which legitimizes *all* forms of subordination for ever. Indeed, biogenetically, the point to grasp is that natural selection will reward *any* form of hierarchy — including the subordination of men to women — if it serves the purposes of gene-replication and the nurture of children. We can put it more strongly: it is clearly a creation principle that organisms are rewarded if they can monitor their changing environments and adapt, even if these adaptations involve the contradiction of inherited and treasured strategies.

This is the situation in which we find ourselves. It is now obvious that successful gene-replication and the nurture of children do not depend on the cultural protection of religious systems. Therefore, a major issue for religions has become how to change the laws, attitudes, and customs which have lost their original function. Religions have now become increasingly detached from the original baseline considerations of protecting gene-replication and the nurture of children, in the sense that, in technological, industrial societies, they are no longer the primary context of protection and control. The transition is proving to be particularly painful because, although religions rest, in any case, on the many achievements they have made through the long process of somatic exploration, they nevertheless are still deeply involved in issues concerning the family. There is, thus, a strong cultural lag in this area, with religions still wishing to maintain controls and definitions which were appropriate to a world that no longer exists. This, as we will see, is particularly apparent in the ways in which religions continue to try to operate the lives of women on the basis of arguments derived from nature and culture.

The cultural definition of women

One might suppose, of course, that the days are gone when we could define the natural nature of women with the confidence of Dr Johnson — 'Sir, a woman's preaching is like a dog's walking on its hinder legs: it is not done well; but you are surprised to find it done at all' — or of Martin Luther — 'Men have broad shoulders and narrow hips, and accordingly they possess intelligence. Women have narrow shoulders and broad hips. Women ought to stay at home. The way they were created indicates this, for they have broad hips and a wide fundament to sit upon, keep house and bear and raise children.'

Those days are gone — or are they? In fact, the social and cultural definition of women, still controlled by men, continues much as before, and the fact that the debate about the ordination of women takes place in this context is simply a part of the way in which the world legitimately sets the agenda for the Church — not even the Vatican thinks that the prophetic stand demanded of the Church is to maintain the *status quo* in the way in which men treat women.

Take — as an example of what this definition of women by men means in practice — a single day, 7 July, 1992. On that day, the *Independent* carried a report under the headline, 'Fears that 10,000 Girls Face Threat of Circumcision'. We are talking here, not of ten thousand girls around the world, but ten thousand girls in the UK, most of them aged eight or under. Around the world, something like eighty million women may have suffered in this way.

7 July was also the day when the Garrick Club voted not to admit women as members. It is not in question that there are men who prefer the company of other men in their leisure time; it is the arguments put forward to justify the vote that are noteworthy. Thus, Leo Cooper, a publisher said:

> I am against. I joined a man's club — if you join a cricket club you expect the members to be cricketers; if you join the Liberal club, you expect the members to be liberal.

To which one might add that if you join a club founded, as the Garrick club was, for 'bringing together the patrons of drama and its professors', you might expect the members to include actresses as well as actors. However, Mr Cooper concluded, 'It's nothing to do with sex — it's to do with intellect.'

That may explain the argument of Derek Nimmo: 'It was a private club matter, and the result was satisfactory. I just wanted it to remain a gentleman's club because I don't think women are clubbable.' This is a pure and unsullied example of the argument addressed to nature and creation principles, that there is a fixed, known, and invariable 'nature of women' which is incompatible with a fixed, known, and invariable nature of clubbability. It is, therefore, in the interests of women themselves not to attempt to do what they are, by nature, incapable of doing.

That, at least, was the argument of Frank Muir: 'It's an amusing issue. Not important at all. I can't imagine why women would ever want to join. It's full of boring old men . . . . I suppose I'm against it in a mindless sort of way, partly because it's verging on the politically correct movement.'

And, still on 7 July, it was the morning after the first episode of the new BBC 'soap', *Eldorado*. All critics were agreed that it was an awe-inspiring catastrophe. Richard Last, having commented that 'Verity Lambert's £10 million infant seems to be tunnelling its way back to the standards of *Crossroads*', added:

> More sinister than any of this, *Eldorado* looks to me like yet another manifestation of the feminist conspiracy now rampant within television. It cannot be mere coincidence that virtually all the male characters are layabouts or villains, and virtually all the females are victims who do the essential work, like running the bar and the massage parlour.

Note the definition of what is essential work, and, even more, of what is sinister — 'the feminist conspiracy now rampant within television'. Yet, on 7 July, the Broadcasting Standards Commission issued its report, and its Chairperson, William Rees-Mogg, claimed exactly the opposite. Under the headline, 'Male-dominated TV is Alien to Women', he said:

Women feel TV is made by men for women. Far more
women feel it's an alien force coming into their houses representing standards, values and interests they don't share.
The imagination of TV is dominated by male attitudes,
male fantasies.

How do we decide which of those two incompatible opinions
is correct? In a hard-hitting book, *Backlash: The undeclared war against women* (London, Chatto and Windus,
1992), Susan Faludi has made the point that we can never
find out, because it is male-dominated media institutions
which tell us what women and feminism are. It is male-
dominated institutions which talk about feminist conspira-
cies and the harm women are doing to themselves by
seeking such wildly inappropriate goals as membership of
the Garrick Club. Or ordination. For, among those male-
dominated institutions are religions, including most parts
of the Christian Church.

In the past, as we have seen, there may have been natural
wisdom in this, defining 'natural' according to the criteria
of evolutionary success. The ways in which the roles of men
and women have been defined in the past 'according to
nature' have been in accord with what nature, by way of
evolution and natural selection, has allowed. However,
'nature' does not fix these definitions for ever. The definitions have been a social arrangement, a social construction.
They are a response to particular circumstances which
lasted for many thousands of years, but which are now,
quite clearly, changing. These social constructions tell us
nothing about a set of fixed and immutable relationships
between the sexes, which, somehow, 'belong' to masculine
and feminine natures, for, as we shall now move on to see,
it is *we* who construct nature at least as much as it con-
structs us, and, if we are wise, we will always change these
constructions when truth demands it, and when our health
and our salvation depend upon it.

Nature and knowledge

We have already begun to see that the nature of the natural is not fixed in some way, so that we can have access to it, and know all about it. To suppose that there is one fixed, natural nature of the universe — or of women — which we can know and describe is exactly that fundamental error which has been rigorously exposed in the history and philosophy of science in recent years. What more truly happens in the sciences is that we construct our understanding of nature, and these constructions are constantly changing. We achieve impressive degrees of reliability, but even our most assured ideas and theories are going to look extremely limited and even wrong to those who look back on them in a hundred years' time. We can thus look back on Newton's account of the universe, and see that it applies in only a limited way, and we can see in what ways it is very different from the account that Einstein gave, as, indeed, his account is different from that of Bohr. But equally, we can see in context how Newton contributed so massively to a credible and reliable account of the universe.

How can these two things — being, so to speak, both right and wrong at one and the same time — come about? Very simply, because the universe does not tell us about itself in any immediate or unequivocal or direct way. The universe is not waiting for us to open the door, go out, take a look at it, and then describe it exactly as it is. Indeed, at the quantum level, when we try to observe something, we change the position or the momentum of what we are trying to observe, and this builds an 'uncertainty principle' into the very exercise of observation. It means, also (to put it briefly), that all our observations of the universe are theory-laden (we already have our predisposing ideas of what we are observing), and all our theories are underdetermined (we never have all the evidence that, in principle, we need). So, yes, there *is* a universe which interacts with us with great consistency, and this alone makes science possible; it sets a limit on justifiable and believable theories. However, *what* the universe is we cannot finally and exhaustively know. Nature is an invitation to deeper understanding, not a dictation of one final and absolute truth.

Faith and knowledge

If we apply this to Christian doctrine, we can see a certain parallel. The faith of the Fathers (as it is so often called), the faith once and for all delivered to the saints, is not a single, fixed, immutable 'thing'. The creeds, the confessions, the encyclicals, are, indeed, articulate responses to data — to 'given things', as the Latin word 'data' implies — to the self-revealing of God. 'What God is' sets a limit on our wise and shareable accounts, but, even with revelation, we could never know exactly, completely and exhaustively what God is. God is an invitation to deeper understanding, never a dictation of one final and absolute truth — not even, as we shall see, with revelation.

This means that the way in which any Christian — let us say Aquinas — appropriates the data (God's self-revelation) is never identical with what has gone before, nor is it identical with what will come after. We, in our day, incorporate the achievement of the past, while correcting what has, indeed, proved corrigible, including, in the case of Aquinas, his extremely defective understanding of the nature of women: 'As regards the individual nature, woman is defective and misbegotten, for the active force in the male seed tends to the production of a perfect likeness in the masculine sex; while the production of woman comes from defect in the active force or from some material indisposition, or even from some external influence, such as that of a south wind, which is moist . . .'. But we do not discard Aquinas, any more than we discard Newton, simply because we can see the limitations of his thought. On the other hand, we are not afraid to go further than they did, not least through the process of correcting whatever needs to be corrected. To quote the famous saying of William of Malmesbury (which Newton himself was fond of quoting), 'We see further than our ancestors because we stand on the shoulders of giants.'

Nature and the ordination of women

If we turn now to arguments against the ordination of women, we can see how deeply embedded they are in the ill-founded 'natural nature' thesis, translated into a creation principle. A well-considered example of such arguments can be found in the Second Report of the House of Bishops to the General Synod of the Church of England, in which opponents of the proposal gave their reasons for their opposition. They tried to rely on the 'natural nature' argument (that there is a fixed and invariable nature of men and women that we can know about), but then they found that the reasons undergirding this argument were disappearing like mist at the rising of the sun, as the following extract makes clear:

> Some of us believe that both the Old and the New Testaments are consistent in upholding the view that women are subordinate to men and that there is an authority of men over women that stems from the order of creation. Those of us who believe this hold that this is the message of Genesis 2, and a message reiterated in the teaching of Paul as seen, for example, in 1 Corinthians 11 and 14 and 1 Timothy 2. The biblical view of women's subordination is not, as was later thought by Aquinas, because the weaker members must be governed by the wiser; nor is it because man is more rational than woman; nor because women are inferior. It is rather that for harmony and stability in life one person must depend upon another for direction. In exercising authority men are characteristically men and in being subject to authority women are characteristically women. This difference in function is built into the order of creation.
>
> *The Ordination of Women to the Priesthood: A second report by the House of Bishops*, copyright © The Central Board of Finance of the Church of England, 1988, p. 70.

The central passage in this argument ('The biblical view . . .' passage) is, quite simply, the death by a thousand cuts, for, if all the reasons for maintaining the subordination of women are abandoned, as the Bishops concede they must be — because they are indeed false, spurious and immoral — then there is no reason in nature why the one person who depends on another for direction, for 'harmony and stability in life' as the Bishops put it, might not be a male depending on a female. We now take this 'direction' for granted in secular life, and also in spiritual life, where many men *do* depend on women for direction (though women are more likely to call it spiritual friendship or counselling or sharing).

This 'death by a thousand cuts' is just as true in Eastern Orthodoxy, as Elisabeth Behr-Siegel has made clear:

> Let us first note that the arguments put forward today against the ordination of women are by and large no longer the same as those used in past centuries. Among contemporary Orthodox theologians, we hardly hear any more arguments based on the inferiority of women and the hierarchy of the sexes (based on the rabbinical exegesis of the second creation story) or of the responsibility of Eve in the Fall. We hear, however, rather paradoxically, arguments based on women's spiritual charisms — which these theologians feel it is their duty to reveal to women. Such thinkers as Evdokimov call on women not to aspire to a ministry that is incompatible with their specific vocation.
>
> *The Ministry of Women in the Church*, Oakwood Publications, 1991, p. 176, referring to P. Evdokimov, *La Femme et la Salut du Monde*, pp. 247ff..

So, all that the opposing Bishops' argument comes down to at this point is that women are, by nature, designed by God to be subordinate to men; they are, by nature, as Derek Nimmo put it, not clubbable. Headship belongs to men and childbearing to women. This creates, they argue, a fundamental creation ordinance that lies objectively in nature and precludes the ordination of women:

> Subordination is a positive gift in creation: exercised with the mutuality of love it reflects order within the Godhead. The principle is to be lived out most clearly within the marriage bond: a man is to be head over his wife and head over the family, but 'the husband must give his wife what is due to her and the wife equally must give the husband his due' (1 Cor. 7.3). This proper combination of subordination and mutuality is to be reflected also in the community: it is not

a curse but rather a blessing. It signifies that there are things which properly belong to one sex and not to the other. Once this principle is acknowledged, some of us believe it follows that priesthood may be one of those things: one aspect of complementarity is that men may properly be priests while women may not. This is balanced by the fact that, for instance, women can be mothers while men cannot. Complementarity does not mean interchangeability. Those of us who hold this view of headship, subordination and complementarity hold that women ought not to be ordained to a priesthood which entails leadership, oversight, headship and the exercise of authority. To so ordain women would be to contradict a fundamental creation ordinance.

(Report *op. cit.*, pp. 70f.).

But this is the kind of 'natural nature', gene-based argument which is totally and irredeemably wrong. What is fixed in nature physiologically (only women *can* be mothers) does not fix all other characteristics as though they can, equally, be derived from nature: 'women *may not* be priests'. It is an elementary point of logic that the 'can' does not entail the 'may', because there is no 'feminine character' and no 'masculine character' fixed, *like* gender-physiology, in nature or in creation that we can know or describe.

To say this is not to deny that there are characteristic behaviours of women and of men that are acquired and endorsed in culture, some of which may have a genetic base. However, there is no fixed and immutable 'nature of women'. Women are not just 'wombs to be protected', as it used to be thought. There is more to the nature of being a woman than that; and, as we deepen our experience and understanding of what this 'more' is, so *we* construct the nature of women in ways that are always open to extension and revision.

It therefore follows that our construction of the nature of women (as of men) is necessarily corrigible through time. Yet, the Bishops who, in the report mentioned earlier, opposed the ordination of women, were maintaining exactly the opposite. They (and those many who have advanced the same argument) were wrong. *How* wrong they are we can see when we look at the extreme absurdity of the ways in which, in the past, the 'natural nature of women' argument has been put forward and applied, for this makes it abundantly clear why this argument is, indeed, false and must be emphatically rejected in our time.

Menstruation and the natural incapacity of women: a nineteenth-century argument

Consider, as an example, the way in which doctors in the nineteenth century believed that there is a connection *in nature* between menstruation and insanity, and how they then applied this claimed natural connection to the definition of what women can and cannot do. Menstruation is a good example, because, like childbirth, it belongs to the physical nature of women and not to that of men. Male doctors (there were no women doctors at the time) decided that menstruation, especially at the times of its inception and cessation, makes women weak and liable to hysteria and insanity. In fact, the very word 'hysteric' comes from the Greek *hustera*, which means 'a womb'. Dr David Davis, the Professor of Obstetric Medicine at University College in London, stated in a textbook in 1841 that, at the times of menarche and menopause, nymphomania was particularly likely to occur. To make this sound more scientific, the condition was given a Latin name, *furor uterinus*.

This connection seemed to be so obviously a part of the natural and immutable character of women that it was felt, at least by some, that no further evidence or argument was required. In *A Treatise on the Nervous Disorders of Women*, Laycock, in 1840, argued:

> Women in whom the generative organs are developed or in action are the most liable to hysterical disease. Indeed, the general fact is so universally acknowledged, and so constantly corroborated by daily experience, that anything in the nature of proof is unnecessary.
>
> Quoted from A. Digby, 'Women's Biological Straitjacket', in S. Mendus and J. Rendall, eds, *Sexuality and Subordination*, London, Routledge, 1989, p. 202.

This claimed connection between the natural nature of women and their greater liability to insanity then became the basis for asserting other disabilities; and this is exactly the structure of the opposing Bishops' argument; 'once this principle is acknowledged', then you can see that women are, by nature, incapable of undertaking certain activities — for the Bishops, of being ordained, for the doctors and others in the nineteenth century, of being educated. That is why Henry Maudsley, in 1874, argued that attempts to 'assimilate the female to the male mind' would not only fail, but would seriously injure the health of women:

> If it be the effect of excessive and ill-regulated study to produce derangement of the functions of the female organization, of which . . . there is great probability, then there can be no question that the subsequent ills mentioned are likely to follow. The important physiological change which takes place at puberty . . . may easily overstep its health limits, and pass into pathological change . . . . Nervous disorders of a minor kind, and even such serious disorders as chorea, epilepsy, insanity, are often connected with irregularities or suspension of these important functions.
>
> 'Sex in Mind and Education',
> *Fortnightly Review*, XXI, 1874.

If, then, girls and women *were* to be educated, separate schools, universities and degree courses would be required which would recognize their vulnerability. On the other hand, would it not be more sensible not to go against the grain of nature, but, instead, to reinforce the natural vocation of women to be wives and mothers? As Clouston, a psychiatrist, asked, 'Why should we spoil a good mother by making an ordinary grammarian?' (quoted from *Sexuality and Subordination*, p. 213). We are back, yet again, with the Bishops, and with the Orthodox, that women have natural gifts or charisms (p. 208), and should not seek to grasp those that are not properly theirs. The objecting Bishops state: 'This [that men may properly be priests while women may not] is balanced by the fact that . . . women can be mothers while men cannot'. This was exactly Clouston's argument, that women have a unique vocation to be mothers:

> Woman cannot fulfill her destiny if her maternal instincts are impaired. The ideals which would exalt culture above motherhood are suicidal and should be abandoned. It will not do to say that women should have a choice . . . to take up culture and intellectual work, whether it has a lessened capacity for motherhood or not.
>
> *Sexuality and Subordination*, pp. 213ff.

Now we reach the truly malevolent structure of the argument. First, you take a universal, or near-universal, characteristic, such as menstruation or motherhood; you then affirm that other characteristics are carried with this physiological universal (in this nineteenth-century case, that women are incapable of education); you then say that only the educated can decide who is capable of receiving education, thereby ensuring that women can never participate in the decisions which affect what they can and cannot do; equally, you make sure that no experiment can take place to find out what would happen if women were to be educated in the same way as men.

With the sharpness of intellect that men maintained she could not possess, Emily Davies made the point with great precision in the mid-nineteenth century:

> Neither the enlightened ladies nor the London University know what the intellectual differences between men and women may be, but what I argue from this is, that *therefore* existing examinations, having recognised standing, had better be thrown open without reservation and let us see what becomes of it. The moment you claim to know what the special aptitudes are . . . , so long as this arbitrary dictation of studies goes on, we have no chance of finding out what women would choose, if they had a free choice, say, between Ancient and Modern languages.

Still less, she might have added, could we have any chance of finding out what women are or are not capable of doing. Referring back to Clouston's claim about the destiny of women, Anne Digby has drawn out the viciousness of this circular argument:

> Clouston's statement revealed the extent to which medical pronouncements could be conditioned by their social context; it provided a fitting crescendo to a century and a half of medical orchestration on the theme of the incommensurability of the sexes. A cultural construction — or, more accurately, reconstruction — of the female was a response to wider changes in society. Liberal assumptions of the Enlightenment required that evidence was needed to justify an inegalitarian denial of social and political rights to women. The constructs of eighteenth-century anatomists and nineteenth-century craniotomists *appeared* to show that fundamental gender differences were due not to nurture but to nature, and that women were permanently below men in the hierarchy of species. It is in this wider context that we can interpret gynaecologists' and psychiatrists' work in Georgian and Victorian Britain — that of providing a biological rationale for gender differentiation in society. By a revealing irony, not only did women not participate in formulating these allegedly scientific judgements, but they also found their access to the medical profession obstructed because of them.

So, it was decided that women are, by nature, incapable of education, since education subverts their natural gifts and character. Hence the objection of Mr Punch, in 1846, to the spread of women's education beyond that which would enable their natural vocation:

> Now, seriously, the only things, I think.
> In which young ladies should instructed be,
> Are stocking-mending, love and cookery —
> Accomplishments that very soon will sink,
> Since Fluxions now, and Sanscrit conversation,
> Always form part of female education.
>
> C. L. Graves, *Mr Punch's History of Modern England*, I,
> London, Cassell, p. 243.

Therefore, because women were held to be incapable of being educated, it followed that there were very few activities women were believed to be capable of undertaking — their nature was too frail, despite the fact that, at this time, some women were hauling coal trucks underground in mines. Women are incapable of being educated; but only the educated can decide what women are capable, by nature, of doing. This self-protective, vicious circularity is exactly what the male establishments of the Roman Catholic and the Orthodox Churches are relying on in the case of the ordination of women. Women are, by nature, incapable of being ordained, but only the ordained can decide who is capable of ordination. The argument is just as vicious and specious in this case as in the other. There is no necessary connection between the natural characteristics of women in relation to their reproductive physiology and some other asserted incapacity in the domain of culture. There is nothing in nature that makes women incapable of education. There is nothing in nature that makes women incapable of ordination. Yet, this did not deter Dr Duckworth, a consulting physician at St Bartholomew's Hospital, from reaching the conclusion, eighty years ago, that women are, by nature, only capable of marrying, of working for the Zenana Missionary Society, and of improving the sanitation of the eastern British Empire:

> I hold and teach, in spite of some modern opinions to the contrary, that after two-and-twenty years of age matrimony is woman's first natural duty . . . . Next to matrimony, or till it comes, I place that special womanly occupation of sick-nursing — . . . a work so womanly and so peculiarly in the line of her life that it constitutes one of the highest qualifications for subsequent marriage and maternity. I do not go with those who claim that women should enter any of the recognised professions, . . . though I make but a single exception to this principle in the case of women who become medically qualified for Zenana mission work in India. I see there one field for fruitful labour in spreading the best forms of Christian civilization and sanitation in our Eastern Empire.
>
> *Views on Some Social Subjects*, London, 1915, pp. 181ff.

Of course, it is easy to look back and think how absurd it is that anyone could define women in such a way that their only role in life, apart from marriage, is improving the sanitation of the British empire — important though that was. The point, though, is that we do not look back on *ourselves*, so to speak, from eighty years on and see how equally absurd are the arguments by which we, in turn, are defining the nature of women and concluding that they cannot be ordained. 'Nature' and 'the natural' are human constructions. *We* decide what the characteristics of 'masculinity' and 'femininity' are, and these constructions change as we understand more wisely (though still corrigibly) what does actually belong in nature, which is diverse. If there *is* a creation principle, it is that God, in the nature that he created, endorses diversity and change. Job saw the point many centuries ago. Nature is a palace of great varieties, but we wreck and ruin it by our narrow-minded definitions and refusals.

So, the human constructions of human nature are increasingly reliable — error is, indeed, corrected — but they still remain corrigible as we never achieve final and complete accounts. However, these human constructions become lethally powerful in the hands of those who *refuse to be* corrected, who get stuck at one stage of human understanding and insist on this as final truth, such people as bishops, dictators, and popes. They become lethally powerful, because they are used as instruments of power by one group against another. In this case, it is by one half of the human race against the other.

This is the title of William Thompson's prophetic cry against the abuse of the 'natural nature' argument, as long ago as 1825: *Appeal of One Half of the Human Race, Women, Against the Pretensions of the Other Half, Men, to Retain Them in Political, and thence in Civil and Domestic Slavery*. Would that popes and cardinals would listen. Thompson did not deny that men are, by nature, stronger than women: 'Man has not given himself that superiority of physical organisation.' What Thompson argued is that this is no basis for adding cultural differences as though they belong to the same inalienable nature:

> They [women] expect no removal of natural bars to their success. All they ask is that to these natural bars in the way of their pursuit of equal happiness with men, no additional bars, no factitious restraints shall be superadded . . . . They ask every facility of access to every art, occupation, profession, from the highest to the lowest, without one exception to which their inclination and talents may direct and may fit them to occupy. They ask the removal of all restraints and exclusions not applicable to men of equal capacities. They ask for perfectly equal political, civil and domestic rights.

As it was, the choice confronting many women, in Thompson's view, was one of slavery or starvation. Men, in his day, could enter marriage voluntarily; women, in effect, could not: 'The great majority of adult women must marry on whatever terms their masters have willed, or starve.'

If they did marry, though, the woman would have to promise to obey her husband, a promise not even exacted from a slave. A woman, he wrote, 'renounces the voluntary direction of her own actions in favour of the man who has admitted her to the high honour of becoming his involuntary breeding machine and household slave'.

Nature and the justification of slavery

Thompson's comparison with slavery is extremely apt. In the long battle to emancipate slaves and to abolish slavery, we find the same basic arguments in opposition as we find now in the opposition to the ordination of women: first, black people are designed *by nature* to be what they are (i.e., apt to be slaves); second, it is a creation principle, evident in the institution of society, that some were created to serve others; third, this is confirmed in the Bible, where, at the root of history and civilization, Noah proclaims, 'Accursed be Canaan [the descendants of Ham], he shall be his brothers' meanest slave' (*Genesis* 9.25); and, fourth, it would clearly be inopportune to emancipate slaves, as they are really better off conforming to their own nature, provided they are Christianized, because then they will be looked after better than they could care for themselves.

Once again, the arguments may seem incredible, but they are no more incredible than the arguments, which they so closely resemble, of those who argue against the ordination of women. Thus, John van Evrie, a Washington physician, appealed to both nature *and* creation in order to demonstrate that 'the Negro is a man, but a different and inferior species of man', much as it used to be claimed that a woman is 'a sort of infant':

> The Negro is a man, but a different and inferior *species* of man, who could no more originate from the same source as ourselves, than the owl could from the eagle, or the shad from the salmon, or the cat from the tiger; and who can no more be forced by *human power* to manifest the faculties, or perform the purposes assigned by the Almighty Creator to the Caucasian man, than can either of these forms of life be made to manifest faculties other than those inherent, *specific*, and eternally impressed upon their organization.
>
> We are no defender of 'materialism', and utterly reject the impious doctrine, that the human soul is the *result* of organization, and therefore, perishes with it; but the identity of organism and functions, of structure and faculties, of form and capabilities, in short of *specific* organization and a *specific* nature, is a *fact* universal, invariable and indestructible.
>
> The Caucasian brain measures 92 cubic inches — with the cerebrum, the centre of the intellectual functions, relatively predominating over the cerebellum, the centre of the animal instincts; thus, it is capable of indefinite progression, and transmits the knowledge of experience acquired by one generation to subsequent generations — the record of which is history.
>
> The Negro brain measures from 65 to 70 cubic inches — with the cerebellum, the centre of the animal instincts relatively predominating over the cerebrum, the centre of the intellectual powers; thus, its acquisition of knowledge is limited to a single generation, and incapable of transmitting this to subsequent generations, *it can have no history*. A single glance at eternal and immutable *facts*, which

perpetually separate these forms of human existence will be
sufficient to cover the whole ground.

> J. H. van Evrie, *Negroes and Negro Slavery: The first an*
> *inferior race — the latter its normal condition*,
> Baltimore, 1853, pp. 28 ff.

In another example, James Hammond put forward the
'mudsill theory' which claimed that all societies rest on the
mudsill foundation of a class with a naturally lower order
of intellect, and that Scripture endorses this by not contest-
ing slavery and by observing the providential disposition of
God in ensuring that 'the poor ye have always with you':

> In all social systems there must be a class to do the menial
> duties, to perform the drudgery of life. That is, a class
> requiring but a low order of intellect and but little skill. Its
> requisites are vigor, docility, fidelity. Such a class you must
> have, or you would not have that other class which leads
> progress, civilization, and refinement. It constitutes the
> very mud-sill of society and of political government; and you
> might as well attempt to build a house in the air, as to
> build either the one or the other, except on this mud-sill.
> Fortunately for the South, she found a race adapted to that
> purpose to her hand. A race inferior to her own, but emi-
> nently qualified in temper, in vigor, in docility, in capacity
> to stand the climate, to answer all her purposes. We use
> them for our purpose, and call them slaves. We found them
> slaves by the common 'consent of mankind,' which, according
> to Cicero, '*lex naturae est*.' The highest proof of what is
> Nature's law. We are old-fashioned at the South yet; slave
> is a word discarded now by 'ears polite;' I will not charac-
> terize that class at the North by that term; but you have it;
> it is there; it is everywhere; it is eternal.
>
> The Senator from New York said yesterday that the
> whole world had abolished slavery. Aye, the *name*, but not
> the *thing*; all the powers of the earth cannot abolish that.
> God only can do it when he repeals the *fiat*, 'the poor ye
> always have with you;' for the man who lives by daily labor,
> and scarcely lives at that, and who has to put out his labor
> in the market, and take the best he can get for it; in short,
> your whole hireling class of manual laborers and 'operatives,'
> as you call them, are essentially slaves. The difference

between us is, that our slaves are hired for life and well compensated; there is no starvation, no begging, no want of employment among our people, and not too much employment either. Yours are hired by the day, not cared for, and scantily compensated, which may be proved in the most painful manner, at any hour in any street in any of your large towns. Why, you meet more beggars in one day, in any single street of the city of New York, than you would meet in a lifetime in the whole South. We do not think that whites should be slaves either by law or necessity. Our slaves are black, of another and inferior race. The *status* in which we have placed them is an elevation. They are elevated from the condition in which God first created them, by being made our slaves. None of that race on the whole face of the globe can be compared with the slaves of the South. They are happy, content, unaspiring, and utterly incapable, from intellectual weakness, ever to give us any trouble by their aspirations.

   J. H. Hammond, speech reported in *Congressional Globe*,
          35th Congress Session, I, 962, March 4, 1858.

And, with perhaps what seemed the most conclusive argument, George Fitzhugh claimed that 'the Negro is but a grown up child, and must be governed as a child' — there is a natural headship and authority. As a slave, therefore, he is happier than he would be if he had not been made a slave: 'In Africa or the West Indies, he would become idolatrous, savage and cannibal, or be devoured by savages and cannibals.' So, he asserted:

The negro slaves of the South are the happiest, and, in some sense, the freest people in the world. The children and the aged and infirm work not at all, and yet have all the comforts and necessaries of life provided for them. They enjoy liberty, because they are oppressed neither by care nor labor. The women do little hard work, and are protected from the despotism of their husbands by their masters. The negro men and stout boys work, on the average, in good weather, not more than nine hours a day. The balance of their time is spent in perfect abandon. Besides, they have their Sabbaths and holidays. White men, with so much of license and liberty, would die of ennui; but negroes luxuriate

in corporeal and mental repose. With their faces upturned
to the sun, they can sleep at any hour; and quiet sleep is the
greatest of human enjoyments. 'Blessed be the man who
invented sleep.' 'Tis happiness in itself — and results from
contentment with the present, and confident assurance of
the future.

H. Wish, ed., *Ante-Bellum: The writings of George Fitzhugh
and Hinton Rowan Helper on slavery*, New York,
Putnam, 1960, pp. 113ff.

It is important to remember that there was some warrant
for some of these arguments. For example, the book *Time
Under The Cross* evoked passionate debate when it produced statistics to show that slaves were, in some respects
(in terms of health, education, and life-expectation), better
off as slaves. There might be some warrant of the same
kind for showing that women are 'better off' under male
control, but the factual errors alone make the arguments
completely false and wrong, even though some examples of
advantage can be found. In the end, slavery was abolished,
though not without ferocious opposition on the part of
Christians who appealed to nature, creation, Scripture, and
the inopportune moment, just as some Christians do now
in resisting the ordination of women.

In a kind of last-ditch resistance, the claim is then usually
made that there is no parallel between the two. Dr Beckwith,
for example, claimed exactly this, on the grounds that
'slavery is not part of the order of nature, whereas male
headship is' and that the Bible merely tolerates slavery,
but commands male headship in the family and in the
Church. However, we have seen that male headship is no
more 'in nature' than slavery is. Nature will endorse any
strategy that protects gene-replication and the nurture of
children, as both slavery and male headship have done in
the past; and that is why they were written into Scripture
at the time when Scripture was being written. The place of
Scripture in these debates we will come to in due course,
but, first, we have to consider the quite different possibility
that, even if the 'natural nature' argument fails (as it
most certainly does), culture (family and the Church) has,

nevertheless, made a proper division of responsibility between men and women, offering to each the roles and vocations that are appropriate to them. In a religious culture (so the argument usually goes), the differences between men and women are respected, but they each have their own vocations. They are different, but equal, and, in consequence, 'such thinkers as Evdokimov call on women not to aspire to a ministry that is incompatible with their specific vocation' (see p. 208).

Christian culture and the saints

The argument that culture defines roles and responsibilities (so that all are equal, but different) does not depend on a 'natural nature' argument being correct, although it is often connected with it. If, as we must, we give up the latter, the former can still be stated, because culture is not, as we have seen at length, in a one-to-one correspondence with the genes. Thus, it is frequently stated (as by Evdokimov p. 208) that women have special vocations, and that they can achieve excellence in these which is equal to that of men. An obvious example lies in the vocation and achievement of saints.

To become a saint is clearly a possibility for women in Christianity — so much so that, in those parts of Christianity which formally define and canonize saints, women are prominent. It was one of the main reasons why the American writer and poet, Phyllis McGinley became a saint-watcher. She had no doubt about the prevailing cultural attitudes of men towards women, as one of her poems makes clear:

> I learned in my credulous youth
>> That women are shallow as fountains:
> Women make lies out of truth
>> And out of a molehill their mountains.
> Women are giddy and vain,
>> Cold-hearted or tiresomely tender;
> Yet nevertheless I maintain
>> I dote on the feminine gender.

For the female of the species may be more deadly than the
    male
But she can make a cup of coffee without reducing
The entire kitchen to a shambles.

Perverse though their taste in cravats
    Is deemed by their lords and their betters,
They know the importance of hats
    And they write you the news in their letters.
Their minds may be lighter than foam,
    Or altered in haste and in hurry,
But they seldom bring company home
    When you're warming up yesterday's curry.

And when lovely woman stoops to folly
She does not invariably come home at 4 a.m.
Singing 'Sweet Adeline'.

Women hang clothes on their pegs
    Nor groan at the toil and the trouble.
Women have rather nice legs
    And chins that are guiltless of stubble.
Women are restless, uneasy to handle,
    But when they are burning both ends of the scandal
They do not insist with a vow that is votive,
How high are their minds and how noble the motive . . . .
    Yes, I rise to defend
        The quite impossible She.
    For the feminine gend–
        Er is OK by me.

Besides, everybody admits it's a Man's World
And just look what they've done to it.
                        (*Times Three*, New York, 1960, pp. 225f.)

Phyllis McGinley wrote an engaging book called *Saint-Watching* (Chicago, Thomas More, 1982), which she began by saying: 'I know that I am a hero-worshipper, and saints have become the heroes I choose to stare at for the sheer excitement of their achievements as well as for their charms, crotchets, and eccentricities' (p. 3). One reason for this enthusiasm lay in the fact that the paths of holiness could be trodden by women as well as by men. The discipleship of equals is not an aspiration but a fact among the company of saints:

> From the beginning of the Christian era women, no matter what their position in society, knew another outlet for their talents beside the purely domestic. They had only to step from the hearth to the cloister and find there a bracing freedom. If we wish to catch a glimpse of the New Woman as typified in a different age, we need look no further than the female saints. From old abbesses of desert monasteries to the nineteenth century's Mother Javouhey — whom Louis-Philippe of France called 'that great man' — there they stand, articulate, vigorous and unsubduable. Some of them were queens; some of them were peasants. They lived in times of storm or of calm. They were as well-educated as Hilda or as illiterate as Catherine of Siena. But not one of them seems to have found her sex a barrier to greatness.
>
> p. 92.

The argument, therefore, seems obvious, that women do not need to obliterate the distinctions between female and male by seeking ordination to the priesthood because they already have their distinct vocations and charismatic gifts through which they can attain the highest goal of sainthood. This is the only transformation of human nature that matters, ultimately, and it is, in its achievement, independent of gender.

However, this argument, also, needs extremely careful attention. For who decides what counts as a saint, and by what routes this condition is attained? To answer 'God' in the context of a religious system like a Church is clearly facile. John Mecklin illustrated, long ago, how the characterization of what counts as a saint reflects the changing values of European society, so that the virtues which constitute sanctity in one age are not identically those of another (*The Passing of a Saint: A study in culture types*, University of Chicago Press, 1941).

That perception has now been extended and developed with immense detail, which shows the extent to which sainthood is yet another manifestation of patriarchal control. If women can be saints, it is only on the terms that men set and allow. Thus, Weinstein and Bell (in *Saints and Society*, University of Chicago Press, 1982) took a sample of saints between the years 1000 and 1700 in order to establish the parameters within which the achievements and recognition of sanctity actually fell. From their work, it is clear that there never was a 'discipleship of equality', even in numerical terms. Overall, only one in five saints was a woman. This proportion was higher from the thirteenth to fifteenth centuries, rising at its highest point to a quarter, but it sank back in the seventeenth century to less than one in five.

By then, the Reformation had occurred, which placed emphasis on the priesthood of all believers, and on God's grace, available to all sinners. It carried with it a mistrust of the cult of the saints and on the formation of a spiritual élite. On the other side, in the Counter-Reformation, the male hierarchy and control of spiritual power was becoming as dominant as it is today. So Weinstein and Bell concluded:

If the Catholic Reformation recalled the church to the founder's admonition to 'feed my sheep,' it interpreted that duty by establishing a patron-client relationship rather than a brotherhood in the body of Christ. The key to reassertion of clerical authority was a theological doctrine, the role of the sacraments in the process of justification and salvation. Catholicism responded to the Protestant challenge by emphasizing more emphatically than ever before the centrality of the sacraments, and therefore the indispensable mediating role of the priest. The Mass was reaffirmed as a sacrifice that could be performed only by an ordained priest who, at the altar and with his back to the congregation, presided over the miracle of transubstantiation. Whereas in the rest of Christendom the equality of the community of believers came to be symbolized by the sharing of the Lord's Supper, in Catholicism the priest first drank from the cup, then bestowed the wafer on passive communicants. To be sure, this had been Catholic practice for centuries; but in the preceding period lay piety had encroached upon the priestly function and in some cases questioned it outright. Now, challenged by new churches and sects that asserted the priesthood of all believers, Reformation Catholicism rejected all such experiments with religious democracy and reaffirmed the most extreme version of clerical authority and practice.

pp. 27f.

It is true that there was, in the Catholic reformation, a renewed emphasis on the religious life, to which women were indeed invited. However, it was still under male control: in the case of women, their confessors were men, their judges in the Inquisition were men, and any idiosyncracy they exhibited was rapidly judged by men to be enthusiastic and undesirable. The male hierarchy and control of spiritual power remained dominant. Only the male priest could mediate the transubstantiation of bread and wine into body and blood; only the priest could pronounce the absolution of sins; and what this meant by way of control through confession, penance, and absolution has been revealed in the outstanding study by John Mahoney, *The Making of Moral Theology* (Oxford, Clarendon Press, 1987).

The practices were not new; what was new was the emphasis. Where Protestants were affirming the priesthood of all believers, Tridentine or Reformed Catholicism rejected all such experiments with religious democracy and reaffirmed the most extreme version of clerical authority and practice. These reforms were not exactly favourable to women. They could not be ordained, and they were excluded even more from the life and order of the Church — except in those religious enclaves which the men allowed. As Weinstein and Bell comment:

> These reforms were inherently if not consciously unfavourable to women: barred from ordination, women were excluded from the clergy and, to the degree that the clergy and religion became synonymous, were excluded from important aspects of Catholic Reformation piety as well. A Teresa of Avila or a Caterina dé Ricci was still a possibility, but when women attempted to go beyond the tightly restricted sphere allotted to them they encountered serious obstacles. Only the most extraordinary of their gender chose to fight against such obstacles. Most probably never thought of doing so.

p. 226.

At all stages, therefore, it was the men who set the values and controlled the different routes to holiness. It was men who defined the nature of women in relation to holiness. In the *Vitae* (the Lives) of the male saints, women, apart from mothers and sisters, are usually portrayed as limbs of Satan. Women exist in order to enhance the stature of the saint by making unavailing attempts to seduce him into sin. Read dispassionately, the *Vitae* are the soft pornography of their day, produced before the age of videos for the consolation of the celibate clergy. As such, they reinforced and perpetuated the deeply destructive image of women which goes back to the estimate of Eve, and continues into the counsels of the Vatican — and of other Christians — down to the present day.

The *Lives* of the women saints reveal the other side of the same coin, and one that has had equally pernicious consequences. Here, women as saints are constructed in the image of Mary, virgin in spirit and preferably in body as well, longing to escape from the impurities of the world, but assailed far more by temptations arising within the body.

This means that, for men and for women, temptations arise in utterly different ways, which require different lifestyles in order to overcome them — all this, of course, determined by men. Men could see the primary obstacles to their sanctity arising outside themselves in the world and in the activity of the devil, who uses instruments (including women but not confined to women) to subvert them. Weinstein and Bell (p. 86) quote the example of St Philip Neri, who, on his way to pray in the Basilica of the Lateran, caught sight of a half-naked beggar near the Coliseum:

> The man's nude body aroused Philip to impure thoughts that by the grace of God he succeeded in dispelling with prayer. If his sexual excitement caused him any guilt, Philip banished it by asserting that his temptations came not from the naked flesh, but from the devil who had disguised himself as a beggar.

For women, though, the source of sin and downfall comes from within their already weak and sin-full body:

> By contrast, in the lives of female saints sin usually appeared to arise from the depths of woman herself. The devil was not so much a foreign enemy (assaulting the ramparts of godly virtue) as a domestic parasite boring from within, feeding upon the weakness of his female host. While male saints often were gifted with a special form of clairvoyance that enabled them to sniff out the faintest odor of sin in their fellows, it was woman's part to root out the evil within herself rather than to act as champion of morality and censor of the hidden sins of others. In the world of the spirit as in the world of the flesh, men and women were different and unequal.
>
> p. 236.

Because, therefore, men determine the nature of sin, they determine also that the routes to holiness will be different and very much under their control, as Weinstein and Bell make clear:

> The ideal type we discussed in answering the question 'Who was a saint?' might well have been separated into males and females, for nothing so clearly divided the ranks of the saints as gender. Our analysis of conversion showed that the path to the holy life was markedly different for girls and for boys. This divergence widened rather than narrowed as aspiring boys and girls became holy men and women. Moreover, cultic veneration, even as it began during the saint's lifetime and as it flourished at the tomb and in the memory of believers, continued to be sex-differentiated. Men and women did different things in their holy lives, and different values were placed on what they did, both by the faithful and by the church. As we shall show, women were more rigidly confined to a particular type of holiness than were men.
>
> p. 220.

Even much earlier, when pre-feudal Europe had offered to at least some women those opportunities of power and

responsibility which have left their mark on such place-
names as Wolverhampton, this did not flow over into the
communion of saints. Thus, Jane Schulenberg has made an
analysis of saints (comparable to that of Weinstein and
Bell) for the earlier period, from about 500 to 1200, 'Sexism
and the Celestial Gynaeceum' (*Journal of Medieval History*,
IV, 1978, pp. 117–33). Overall, the conclusion is much the
same. Despite claims of 'spiritual egalitarianism' by the
Church, it was much more difficult for women to be recognized as saints than it was for men. However, there is one
difference: there were some periods, especially in the middle of what are known colloquially as the Dark Ages, when
the percentage of women saints was much higher. In a
later article, 'Female Sanctity: Public and Private Roles, ca.
500–1100' (in M. Erler and M. Kowaleski, eds, *Women and
Power in the Middle Ages*, Athens, University of Georgia
Press, 1988), Schulenberg argued that this arises because
of the necessary decentralization of power during those
time of invasion and threat:

> During this early period, in the absence of strong impersonal
> governmental institutions, royal or aristocratic families
> assumed the political, economic and social authority in
> various areas of Europe. Thus within the context of the
> irregular powers of the early medieval family, women could
> achieve positions of authority and control over wealth . . . .
> It is therefore within the context of the household that a
> substantial number of noblewomen and queens of the
> Anglo-Saxon and Merovingian period achieved sainthood.
>
> p. 105.

Not only was this the case, they exercised actual authority,
frequently over men — for example, as abbesses over joint
communities of monks and nuns. They were *consociae* with
kings, participating in the *curia regis*. And, as Schulenberg
observed, 'It is of special interest to note that at this time
we do not find churchmen questioning the propriety of the
roles which these public and powerful female figures had
assumed. Instead they were praised for acting *non
mulieriter sed viriliter*' (p. 114).

But there, exactly, is the rub; acting, not in a womanly

way, but in a way appropriate for men. It is Louis-Philippe searching for the highest praise he can find for Mother Javouhey (p. 223) and calling her, 'that great man'. In the ecclesiastical forum, it is still the male-controlled Church which is operating a male-constructed understanding of the natural nature of women. Even in the middle of this so-called 'golden age for women', the Council of Nantes, in 895, was saying of the legal process:

It is astounding that certain women, against both divine and human laws, with bare-faced impudence, act in general pleas and with abandon exhibit a burning passion for public meetings, and they disrupt rather than assist, the business of the kingdom and the good of the commonweal. It is indecent and reprehensible, even among barbarians, for women to discuss the cases of men. Those who should be discussing their woolen work and weaving with the residents of the women's quarters, should not usurp the authority of senators in public meetings just as if they were residents of the court.

Schulenberg concluded, therefore, that this period, seemingly of most equal opportunity, was, in reality, a period of restricted concession:

The patterns of change which we have been tracing concern an elite group of women, 'women worthies,' who were honored by the Church in their saints' lives and popular cults. While a collective study of the vitae provides many important insights into shifts in female sanctity, the lives furnish only very limited and indirect evidence, for example, about women who actively challenged or defied the growing sex-based restrictions of the Church and society, about informal female influences and networks of power, or about lower-class women. Thus in light of the limitations of our sources and the complexity of female experiences in medieval society, we need to be careful not to attribute a wider validity to these patterns of visibility and status than they merit.

Nevertheless, it appears that in barbarian Europe of the early Middle Ages, women enjoyed a certain potentia and indeed wider opportunities in the 'public' realm as confirmed

by their selection to the celestial gynaeceum. In this pioneering society, when the very survival of the Church
depended on the contribution and cooperation of everyone,
restrictions upon the activities of the allegedly inferior sex
were ignored or temporarily abated. Women with power
and property were actively recruited by churchmen to aid in
missionary work, to establish churches, monasteries, and
centers of education, and to assume positions of leadership
with very real power. They partook of the prerogatives and
privileges of the newly Christianized lands and were frequently rewarded for their essential contributions through
recognition of sanctity.

Although during the golden age of female sanctity (which
is set in the midst of the so-called Dark Ages) the Church
and society acknowledged women's worth (as witnessed by
the relatively high percentage of female saints for the
period), they still failed to recognize their equivalence fully.
This failure is highlighted by the asymmetrical patterns
which emerge from our survey of the dossiers of female and
male saints.

Even on a less exalted scale, among nuns who did not
become saints, the research of Penelope Johnson (on nunn-
eries in northern France, *Equal In Monastic Profession*,
Chicago University Press, 1994) has shown that the earlier
symmetry between the monastic lives of women and men
had already been eroded by the middle of the twelfth
century.

It is clear, therefore, that women were always presented
with a far more limited range of options, and that they
were thought to be peculiarly vulnerable to subversion by
the Devil and his agents. Weinstein and Bell went further
and argued that women internalized the religious system's
misogyny and began to believe it about themselves. As a
result, 'they were more likely than men to turn to the
supernatural to work some particular effect; if they were
successful, their neighbours were quick to suspect them of
witchcraft or, much less often, to venerate them as saints'
(p. 228).

What, then, of witches? Was this at least one domain
where women could make a declaration of independence

from men? In terms of the modern understanding of Wicca, it is clear that the continuity of an ancient wisdom was certainly a route to power of a sort, though a precarious one at most times, but even here, it was still predominantly men who controlled the designation and treatment of witches. Thus, even in the Protestant churches, which were inclined to regard the promotion and adoration of saints with extreme suspicion, women were by no means better off. In a book on social deviancy among Puritans in the New England settlement of the seventeenth century (*Wayward Puritans: A study in the sociology of deviance*, New York, Macmillan, 1986), Kai Erikson has shown how men controlled the lives of women through the definition of deviancy, not just in the familiar case of the Salem witches, but also in the earlier antinomian dispute and in the contest with the Quakers.

The antinomian dispute is of particular interest, because it arose from the claim of a woman, Mrs Hutchinson, that only those ministers who are living in the covenant of grace — of which she could find few examples in New England — have authority. She therefore followed the command of the *Epistle to Titus*, which says that the elder women should instruct the younger. So there were soon gathered at her house (of course she could not speak in the church building, and she took that biblical command seriously as well) a large company who admired both her theological acumen and (as even Winthrop acknowledged) 'her nimble wit and active spirit' (p. 77). For this threat to male authority in her teaching, she was regarded as culpable: she was excommunicated and banished from the community. As Winthrop remarked in his Journal:

> If she had attended her household affairs, and such things as belong to women, and not gone out of her way and calling to meddle in such things as are proper for men, she had kept her wits, and might have improved them usefully and honorably in the place that God had set her.
>
> Quoted from Erikson, p. 82.

At both the extremes, the Catholic and the Protestant, which were so passionately divided from each other, there is a bond of unity in their determination to keep women in their restricted and God-determined place. Yet, even so, women resisted this domination of their lives in remarkable ways. Even though men set the boundary conditions of value and appropriate living, women nevertheless created their own lives of value and action within these boundaries. This took them far beyond the usual threshold which observes that women exercised private influence as a substitute for public power. Women made their own kind of success, on their own terms, out of the cultural and symbolic values available to them.

Holy feast and holy fast

This is a point strongly urged by Caroline Walker Bynum, in *Holy Feast and Holy Fast* (Berkeley, University of California Press, 1987), exploring 'the religious significance of food to medieval women'. The religious goals of holiness raise the issue of control: who operates my life? Is it the Holy Spirit or the Devil? Is it desires of the world and of the flesh, or is it the desire for God? Asceticism, understood as renunciation, is a quintessential demonstration of priority and control. Men can demonstrate asceticism by renouncing power and espousing humility because they, after all, are the ones who have access to power, so they are in a position to renounce it. But women do not have that opportunity. Over what do they have a corresponding control, which they can renounce? One answer, as Bynum's book makes clear, is food:

> I have argued that medieval women are not best understood as creatures constrained and impelled by society's notions of the female as inferior. Women's piety was not, fundamentally, internalized dualism or misogyny. Although misogynist writing did certainly sometimes equate *woman* with sexual temptation and underline the male/female contrast as a dichotomy of superior/inferior, strong/weak, spirit/flesh, I consider it mistaken to take the ideas of male theologians and biographers about women as the notions of women about themselves. Women and men existed, of course, in the

same universe of symbols and doctrine and were taught by the same scriptures, the same preaching. Women were clearly aware of their supposed inferiority; some commented upon it or even appropriated it as a way to God . . . . But from among the symbols and doctrines available to them, women and men chose different symbols — men renouncing wealth and power, women renouncing food. They used symbols in different ways. Men, who were dominant, used symbols (among them the male/female dichotomy) to renounce their dominance. Reversals and oppositions were at the heart of how symbols worked for men. The image of woman as contrasted to that of man was, in the later Middle Ages, a topic of primary interest to men. To women, however, male/female contrasts were apparently of little interest; symbols of self were in general taken from biological or social experience and expressed not so much reversal or renunciation of worldly advantage as the deepening of ordinary human experience that came when God impinged upon it. In their symbols women expanded the suffering, giving self they were ascribed by their culture, becoming ever more wonderfully and horribly the body on the cross. They became that body not as flight from but as continuation of self. And because that body was also God, they could sum up their love of God in paradox: 'Hell is the highest name of Love,' as Hadewijch said, or as Margaret Porete put it, 'I am the salvation itself of every creature . . . . For I am the sum of all evils.'

pp. 295ff.

Here we have a classic example of how women create lives on their own terms, even when they are deprived of authority and power. Weinstein and Bell had raised the opposite possibility — that perhaps women had internalized the defective character that men had imposed on them — and, certainly, the twentieth century has made it clear how easily people in desperate circumstances will come to believe and embody what is said about them, and how this then creates a vicious spiral downwards, because the people who have internalized these descriptions of themselves become a living proof of the correctness of the description.

However, in Bynum's view, women did *not* internalize

the misogynistic norms of the patriarchal, controlling society in which they lived: 'Medieval women are not best understood as creatures constrained and impelled by society's notion of the female as inferior; women's piety was not, fundamentally, internalised dualism or misogyny' (p. 295).

In contrast, many women achieved a powerful self-definition through the creation of their own symbolic worlds, focusing on food. And since there happened to be, between the tenth and fourteenth centuries, 'a significant proliferation of opportunities for women to participate in specialised religious roles', we find women in this period actually emancipating themselves from male clerical control; we find them preaching, hearing confessions from other nuns, bestowing blessings, and administering communion to each other in rites known as 'masses without priests'. There was even a brief endeavour to recognize that the redemptive humanity of Jesus must include the feminine — even literally so:

> When we look at male writing in the later Middle Ages we find that symbolic dichotomies and reversals were at its very heart. Men tended to use the male/female dichotomy to underline male/female differences (father versus mother, teacher and disciplinarian versus nurturer, tough versus soft, etc.) and to castigate or romanticize female weakness. As I have demonstrated elsewhere, men tended to associate a clearly delineated set of social and biological characteristics with each gender, even when they were using gender as a symbol, and they tended to see these sets of characteristics as opposites. For example, Guerric of Igny (d. ca. 1157) wrote: 'The Bridegroom [Christ] . . . has breasts, lest he should be lacking any one of all duties and titles of loving kindness. He is a father in virtue of natural creation . . . and also in virtue of the authority with which he instructs. He is a mother, too, in the mildness of his affection, and a nurse.' An anonymous Franciscan, describing Francis and Elizabeth of Hungary as parents of the friars minor, wrote: 'He was the father . . . and she was their mother. And he guarded them like a father, she fed them like a mother.' In their symbolic universe, men tended to use the male/female

dichotomy not only as a symbol of authority/nurture, spirit/flesh, law/mercy, strong/weak, but in a broader sense as a way of expressing the contrast between God and soul, divinity and humanity, clergy and laity. To medieval men, God was (as he has been to most of the pious throughout the long Christian tradition) metaphorically male — father or judge, bridegroom or friend — and the soul (partly because of the linguistic gender of *anima*) was frequently symbolized or described as female. Moreover, the gender dichotomies we find in men's writings were reinforced by other gender dichotomies that were implicit in the ways people lived. Men were food receivers, women food preparers and generators. Men were priests and women laity. Men were authoritative by office or ordination; women's religious power derived from inspiration, from ecstatic visitation.

p. 282.

When Julian of Norwich wrote of God's motherhood of mercy and grace, and of our true mother, Jesus, all love, who bears us for joy and for endless living, we are inclined to marvel at the brilliance of her freedom. Yet she was by no means alone, as Eleanor McLaughlin has illustrated, in an article, 'Christ My Mother: Feminine Naming and Metaphor in Medieval Spirituality', *Nashotah Review*, XV, 1975, pp. 228–48. As Bynum observed, in *Jesus as Mother: Studies in the Spirituality of the High Middle Ages* (Berkeley, University of California Press, 1982), the use of maternal images is not a straightforward transposition of language, but is embedded in the paradoxical tension of all spirituality, which evokes 'both affirmation and rejection of the world, the flesh and the institutions and rules they necessitate' (p. 263). Nevertheless, even though such images may be construed as a particular strategy in a more general spiritual world, they had the effect of challenging clerical authority by offering a more charismatic alternative, and they therefore had the further consequence of replacing the emphasis on God's power with an emphasis on his accessibility.

However, all this evoked, not surprisingly, the extreme opposition of men, especially from those who exercised authority in the system. Even a rapid increase in the number of women's religious houses was seen as a threat:

> The Premonstratensians were the first to pass legislation curtailing women's monasteries; the Cistercians followed. As R. W. Southern has made us aware, misogyny — a male fear of female sexuality that was a projection of male fear of male sexuality — was sometimes the articulated motive for such repression. The notorious opinion, attributed to the Premonstratensian abbot Conrad of Marchtal, that 'the wickedness of women is greater than all other wickedness of the world and . . . the poison of asps and dragons is more curable and less dangerous to men than the familiarity of women' may be spurious. But a number of twelfth-century monastic leaders feared that celibate males would be contaminated by women and were willing to limit women's religious opportunities in order to protect fragile male virtue. Bernard of Clairvaux (d. 1153) warned his monks: 'To be always with a woman and not to have sexual relations with her is more difficult than to raise the dead. You cannot do the less difficult; do you think I will believe that you can do what is more difficult.'
>
> pp. 15ff.

Saints and the denial of humanity

Although this is a restricted and specific example, it is this aggressive cancer, spreading into every cell of the Christian body, which has raised the obvious possibility that, culturally, Christianity is irredeemably patriarchal and misogynist. Even if *nature* does not fix the nature of women, *culture* evidently does; and, given the history of Christian (male) attitudes to women, here surely we can see an insuperable objection to the ordination of women. It is relatively mild to observe that women could only become saints on the terms which men allow, and that sanctity turns out to be yet another instrument of patriarchal domination and control. It is far more radical and subversive to ask who would want to be a saint at all, as Christendom has defined what it means to be a saint on male terms. Saints epitomize the values that Christianity holds up for emulation. But what if these values are, in fact, the diseased pathology of those who say 'No' to life?

This was the searching question asked by Nietzsche and, although it may seem easy to dismiss his anger as extreme, it is nevertheless central to Edith Wyschogrod's analysis of *Saints and Post-Modernism: Revisioning Moral Philosophy* (University of Chicago Press, 1990) that his arguments 'require a response if altruism is to retain its cogency in the context of post-modern thought':

> Perhaps the most powerful critique in Western thought that has been levelled against altruism is Nietzsche's account of it as a hypocritical masking of weakness. . . . As a result of both inner and institutional repression, a new human type is created, the man of *ressentiment*.
>
> pp. 99, 101.

For Nietzsche, the terrifying failure of Christians is that they receive a world, from what they take to be the hand of God, which is full of opportunity for celebration, and they promptly excommunicate as sinners precisely those who do celebrate life and are not frightened to exercise the natural will to power. What he called 'herd morality' is nothing other than 'malice spiritualized', 'the favourite revenge of the spiritually limited against the less limited' (*Beyond Good and Evil*, p. 219). The morality endorsed in any society is itself an expression of someone's 'will to power'; the morality of the Church, exercised through encyclicals, pastoral letters, sermons, schools and the confessional, is unquestionably a bid for power. However, in the case of the Church, this is a morality reacting against the strong, the independent, the exceptional, the flourishing — in relation to all of which the Church feels itself to be threatened (*The Will to Power*, p. 274). Thus, 'the love of one's neighbour' turns out, in fact, to be a *fear* of one's neighbour, an *envy* of one's neighbour, a deep determination that saints shall be those who deny and abdicate from the opportunities of life. As he put it, 'only the modest, submissive, conforming mentality, the mediocrity of desires, attains high moral status and honour' (*Beyond Good and Evil*, p. 221).

Thus, the attitudes of altruism and pity, which Christians

regard as self-evident virtues, arise, in Nietzsche's view, from rage, frustration and resentment. As he put it in *The Genealogy of Morals*, 'Impotence which cannot retaliate is turned into kindness, cowardice into humility'. Christianity, as he observed it at the end of the nineteenth century, is the confirmation of cowardice in conduct, the great reversal of values whereby the life-enhancing possibilities of human freedom are brought under threatening constraint: laws and conscience are invented to reward conformity and to destroy the heretic. This institutional and interior repression produces the human character of *ressentiment*, crabbed and incapable of action except in the direction of self-destruction and defeat.

The maintenance of this distorting cultural system is then achieved through the strong hierarchical structure of Pope, cardinals, archbishops, bishops, and priests (from all of which women are excluded), operating control through encyclicals, confessionals, seminaries and schools. The saint is the seal of approval in the system, summarizing the surrender of the human will, ostensibly to God, but, in fact, to what some men define as God's approval.

In this Nietzschian perspective, who would be a saint? It requires a virtual blasphemy against God, because it calls into question the value of the world and of human competence within the world by embracing them within a comprehensive definition of sin. God's creation becomes the opponent to be beaten down and subjected to a superior will — a will which, in Nietzsche's understanding, has buried itself in a deep bunker of refusal. It sanctifies its refusal by taking its revenge on God by regarding what God has created as a minefield of threat: anything might become the opportunity of sin. Terrified above all of sexuality, sexuality becomes the first sin and the strongest enemy; and, not surprisingly, women cannot be ordained.

All of which, surely, is too extreme? Perhaps. But by how much? Consider this newspaper report of a mass in Westminster Cathedral in 1987:

> Just before Cardinal Hume set off for the West Indies to lead a retreat, he had a Caribbean-style Mass in Westminster

Cathedral. An invitation went out to 'ethnic' altar servers throughout the Diocese of Westminster. One parish priest in the East End of London decided that all his servers qualified, one way or another; and about half of them made the journey down to Victoria. In the Cathedral they vested. Five of them were girls; seven were boys. The girls were denied access to the sanctuary. It was, they were told, against the Cardinal's regulations. The boys, at least from this particular parish, stayed off the altar in solidarity and sat, vested in the front pew throughout the celebrations. It later transpired that other parishes, knowing the ruling against girls serving at the altar in the Cathedral, had decided against sending any of their servers to the service.

This is a deep and enculturated attitude, going far back into feelings about uncleanness — Nietzsche (although he would have used other words) would have called it an enculturated terror. It is an attitude fixed in culture, not in nature, which illuminates the Cardinal's explanation, in the same year, of why he rejected the ordination of women in the Anglican Communion. Intellectually and rationally he could see that the argument that 75 per cent of Christendom do not do so is not an argument at all, although it is, as he put it, an important fact. But, he went on:

> For me the fundamental argument is the sacramental aspect of it. When I take the bread, the host, and say the words in the service of the Mass, I know I have changed it, with the power of Christ, to the body of Christ, and my congregation knows it. But on what authority, if a woman does it, do I know that she has changed it?
>
> *The Independent*, 16 December, 1988, p. 6.

The answer is both simple and obvious: by exactly the same authority which a woman receives at her ordination as does a man. There is no argument here that a woman cannot be ordained, or that only a man can be the representative or icon of Christ, because the Cardinal has already made it clear in his argument that Christ acts *through* the priest, not *as* the priest, and that Christ is present, really and truly, in the elements, not in the one authorized to bring

this presence into the sacrament. Indeed, a subsequent
letter to *The Independent* pointed out that, according to the
New Testament, a woman, without the assistance of any
man whatsoever, brought the *original* body and blood of
Christ into the world, so, the writer asked, 'Why not the
continuing body and blood of Christ in the sacrament?'

It is not, in this Nietzschian perspective, that those who
embody this negativity in their lives cannot be attractive
and humble people — indeed, the argument is that they
are likely to be so. Such people may well be saints. But
saints only as men like themselves define them. It then follows inevitably, in Nietzsche's argument, that, as celibates,
they tell others the meaning of sex; as men, they tell women
what they must not do. When the Pope visited the United
States, a cartoon in *The Washington Post* portrayed him
addressing a vast crowd and saying: 'Women priests, "No";
homosexuals, "No"; contraception, "No"; abortion, "No"; tol-
eration, "Yes".' And, on the fundamentalist side, a group of
women recently summarized the evangelical message to
men: 'God loves you, and He has very bad news for your
wife.'

Is this too one-sided a picture? Of course it is. Even as a
picture of the strongest of religious systems — Roman
Catholicism — it does not do justice to the protest within
its own ranks against the kind of attitude articulated by
Cardinal Hume, a protest all the more agonizing because of
the respect in which he is held. However, the issue will still
remain whether or not change is as possible in the case of
culture as it was in the case of the equally ephemeral argument based on the 'natural nature of women'. It is true that
culture does not determine the status and value of women
in an immoveable way, any more, as we have seen, than
do nature and the genes. However, cultural values and
arrangements are extremely difficult to change when they
have been long-running, not least because those who control them have both the power to make decisions and a
strong personal interest in conserving the *status quo*.

But change in other equally intransigent matters has
proved possible in the past. Consider the text of Paul,

whose exact meaning is (as with all texts) uncertain, but whose general import is clear: 'For you are all the children of God through faith in Christ Jesus, for as many of you as have been baptized have been clothed in Christ. There is neither Jew nor Greek, there is neither slave nor free, there is not male and female' (*Galatians* 3.28). Whether this is referring to the recruitment of converts from all parts of society without discrimination, or whether it is looking to the final vision of what will in the end be the case, there is no doubt what the vision is. The Church has been slow to move towards it.

In the case of 'neither Jew nor gentile', for nearly two thousand years Christians have kept open this division by the practice of an unrelenting anti-Semitism. Even now, they have not entirely eradicated from their souls the malice which leads to murder, but they have at least begun to turn to a restored recognition of the continuing Jewish vocation under God.

In the case of 'neither slave nor free', it took almost two thousand years for Christians to see that the interior logic of God's love could not possibly allow the condition of slavery, even though Scripture clearly envisaged it as a natural state.

What prospect, then, for 'no longer male and female', as worked out in religious society? The prospect, at first sight, must seem good. No one, surely, doubts that the male-controlled Church is capable of deep, radical, open-eyed, unrelenting evil. But the question is whether the Church, founded in a period of patriarchy, really is incapable of change. Clearly it is not *incapable* of change, since it has already *begun* to change. Quite apart from the fact that the vote went in favour of ordaining women in one part of the Church, there are many millions of Christians, including many Roman Catholics, who are realizing already this vision of Paul's, in the way in which they live.

However, across the road stands — or seems to stand — an insurmountable obstacle. The arguments against the ordination of women, which were based on the non-negotiable requirements of nature and of culture, are empty.

But religious systems are not constrained by the success or failure of those arguments alone, if at all. There will always be sources of legitimation within the systems themselves. In the Christian case, 'the Bible says . . .'. If the Bible is 'the Word of God', it is going to be, not subordinate to the process of body-culture coevolution, but, rather, a constant constraint over its direction. If the Bible rules out the ordination of women, then, no matter what changes may have occurred in society, there is no way in which this change could be allowed. But *does* the Bible work in this way or does it have an entirely different relation to the interaction between the Church and the world?

20

The Bible as Cultural Constraint

On 24 February 1791, John Wesley took up his pen and wrote his last letter, less than a week before he died. He wrote it to William Wilberforce, who had already begun his campaign for the abolition of slavery. It was a campaign which Wesley had himself supported with passion in one of his most powerful tracts, *Thoughts upon Slavery*, in 1774. In his letter to Wilberforce he wrote:

My Dear Sir,

Unless the Divine Power has raised you up to be as Athanasius, *contra mundum*, I see not how you can go through your glorious enterprise in opposing that execrable villainy which is the scandal of religion, of England, and of human nature. Unless God has raised you up for this very thing, you will be worn out by the opposition of men and devils; but *if God be for you, who can be against you*? Are all of them together stronger than God? Oh, *be not weary in well doing*. Go on, in the name of God and in the power of His might, till even American slavery, the vilest that ever saw the sun, shall vanish away before it.

Reading this morning a tract wrote by a poor African, I was particularly struck by that circumstance that a man who has a black skin, being wronged or outraged by a white man, can have no redress; it being a *law* in our colonies that the *oath* of a black against a white goes for nothing. What villainy is this!

That He who has guided you from your youth up may continue to strengthen you in this and in all things is the prayer of,

       Dear Sir,

          Your affectionate Servant,

             John Wesley

How could Wesley take up such a strong position on this issue? In his *Earnest Appeal to Men of Reason and Religion*, he took it for granted (in a bracket on p. 2) that the Scripture is of God. To demand the abolition of slavery is to go far beyond what the text of Scripture strictly requires. Slavery in the Bible is natural and belongs to the creation order. So to ameliorate the condition of slaves is one thing, but to abolish the condition altogether is, in some sense, to correct the Bible.

Yet, this is the same Wesley who believed, not only that witchcraft is as real as the Bible says it is, but, even more, that the giving up of witchcraft is, in effect, 'giving up the Bible'. It is easy to see why Wesley argued as he did. He was faced by atheism and materialism, and even by Deism, which he did not regard as being much better. (Deism allowed that there is indeed God who designed the world and gave it its laws, but when God had set the world on its way, he could not, so to speak, get into it and work such things as miracles, because Newton's universe was an entirely predictable mechanism). What Wesley wanted to defend was the Biblical record that there are spiritual realities, which, in his view, would then call materialism in question; and among those spiritual realities are witches. So he wrote:

It is true . . . that the English in general, and indeed most of the men of learning in Europe, have given up all accounts of witches and apparitions, as mere old wives' fables. I am sorry for it; and I willingly take this opportunity of entering my solemn protest against this violent compliment which so many that believe the Bible pay to those who do not believe it. I owe them no such service . . . . They well know (whether Christians know it or not) that the giving up witchcraft is, in effect, giving up the Bible; and they know, on the other hand, that if but one account of the intercourse of men with separate spirits be admitted, their whole castle in the air (Deism, Atheism, Materialism) falls to the ground.

N. Curnock, ed., *The Journals of the*
Rev. John Wesley, A.M., London, 1909–16, V, p. 265;
cf. also p. 375 and VI, p. 109.

In a comparable way, many of those who oppose the ordination of women to the priesthood believe that it would involve 'giving up the Bible', in the sense that it is contrary to Scripture. Thus, a number of clergymen wrote to *The Church Times* on 10 July 1992:

Sir,

We and other clergy are convinced that the proposed legislation to ordain women presbyters is not so much about their presiding at communion as about admitting them to positions of headship in the Church. We are convinced that admitting women to the presbyterate and thus to oversight is contrary to scripture and the revealed will of God for the Church, cultural conditioning notwithstanding.

On what Biblical grounds is this conviction reached? In Genesis 1, it is said that 'God created man in his own image, in the image of God he created him; male and female he created them' (1.27), but, in Genesis 2 and 3, Adam is created *first*, *then* the animal kingdom and the natural world, *then* woman, from a rib extracted from Adam's side. She is to be his helper: 'Your desire shall be for your husband, and he shall rule over you' (Gen. 3.16). For some (to quote further the Report referred to on p. 207), this means that

the creation narratives testify to a subordination of women and [?to] men in the created order itself . . . . It was this tradition of rightful subordination that Paul knew and continued to uphold in his ministry . . . . For some of us, there is a divine ordinance in creation which precludes women being in positions of headship/leadership in the Christian community.

p. 54.

What then of Paul? I Corinthians 11.2–16 assumes that women pray and prophesy in the *ekklesia*, the Church. When a woman does so, she must have a sign of authority (*exousia*) on her head. Even so, she remains derivative from man, for whose sake she was made. Yet, in I Corinthians 14.33–6, this activity of women in the Church appears to be contradicted. The fact that, in some texts, verses 34 and 35 stand *after* verse 40 raises the suspicion that this is a later regulation dropped into the Pauline text. Even so, it stands in the canonical text and, for some, the two passages together demonstrate a dependence of women on men where public speaking and instruction are concerned: 'As in all the churches of God's holy people, women are to remain quiet in the assemblies, since they have no permission to speak: theirs is a subordinate part, as the law itself says.'

This is reinforced by I Timothy 2.11–14, often read in conjunction with II Corinthians 11.3. Because Eve was created second and then introduced sin and its penalty, she 'must be a learner, listening quietly and with due submission: I do not permit a woman to be a teacher, nor must women domineer over men.'

Outside the institutional life of the Church, the subordination of women is mirrored in their relation to their husbands: 'Wives, be subject to your husbands as to the Lord; for the man is the head of the woman, just as Christ also is the head of the Church' (Ephesians 5.22).

Does this catena of quotations mean that women cannot be ordained to what some call the presbyterate and others the priesthood? What do these texts mean?

The meanings of Scripture

The first thing that has to be said about the meaning of Scripture is that no one knows what *the* meaning is, for three related reasons. The first is that no one knows what the original text of Scripture was, meaning by 'original' the text that the author actually wrote. The transmission of the text of Scripture through many centuries has introduced so many variants that there is no way in which anyone could reconstruct some original text as it came from the hand of the writer, no matter how direct the inspiration of the Holy Spirit may have been. Nor are these variants always some innocent accident of transmission. In some instances it is possible to discern a deliberate alteration of the text in order to argue or prove some point. A particularly relevant example of this is the Western text of the Acts of the Apostles, of which Codex Bezae, known as D, is of great importance.

In *The Theological Tendency of Codex Bezae Cantabrigiensis in Acts* (Cambridge University Press, 1966), E. J. Epp makes it abundantly clear that the differences in D amount to a heightened anti-Jewish tendency. It is equally possible to discern a tendency against women. There appears to have been a deliberate attempt to write women out of their place in the early history of the Church. Thus, other texts of Acts 1.14 associate women closely with the eleven disciples: 'With one heart all these joined constantly in prayer, together with certain women, including Mary, the mother of Jesus, and with his brothers.' D adds 'and children', thereby turning this into something resembling a family outing. Similarly, all texts of Acts play down the leadership and fellow worker role of women manifest in Paul's letters, in which he mentions so many women — Prisca, Apphia, Phoebe, Junia, Mary, Tryphaena, Tryphosa, Persis, Euodia and Syntyche. Other texts of Acts recognize the indispensable contribution made by women in support of Christian mission, even though they reduce the role as it appears from Paul's letters. But D goes further. In Acts 17.4, D changes 'and not a few of the leading women' into simply 'women'; and, at the end of chapter 17, the woman convert, Damaris, disappears.

The disparities between Western and other texts of Acts may be an extreme example, but they highlight the problem of meaning, in the sense that there is a radical (i.e., at the root) uncertainty at the very outset of Biblical interpretation. However, let us suppose that we could agree — at least in terms of probability — what the original text is likely to have been. We then come to the second reason why we can never know, definitely and conclusively, what the Bible means: words do not have simple meanings which we can know and translate (see my 'Religious Studies and the Languages of Religions', *Religious Studies*, XVII, pp. 425–39). Take the phrase, much used in the Synod debate, that men and women were alike 'made in the image of God'. It *seems* a straightforward sequence of words, but we do not know what the Hebrew word *zelem* means in this context. It may even be related to the Arabic word *zulma*, 'darkness, overshadowing', so that the text would mean, 'God created them in the shadow of himself', or 'by means of the overshadowing of himself'. However, this is only a possibility. We cannot know conclusively what the phrase means because the possible legitimate meanings even of the words alone are many. Take a relatively simple connection in Romans 5.12, a verse that was translated in the New English Bible as: 'It was through one man that sin entered the world, and through sin death, and thus death pervaded the whole human race, inasmuch as all men have sinned.' The word 'inasmuch' represents two words and three letters in Greek, *eph ho*. In his *Commentary on Romans* (The Anchor Bible, 1993), J. A. Fitzmyer lists eleven different 'meanings' of those two words, each of which is legitimate, and each of which affects the sense greatly, since from this passage important conclusions were drawn in Christian history concerning the nature of original sin. We cannot know conclusively 'what the phrase means'.

Even when something like a consensus concerning meaning has formed, it is not immune from correction or change. Take the words (of importance in the debate about women) *diakonos*, *diakonia*, which are transliterated as 'deacon' and 'diaconate'. Through virtually the whole of Christian history, it has been assumed that the word *diakonos* carries with it an association of service — for example, service at table. A deacon in *Mark* 10.43–5 is parallel to *doulos*, a slave: 'Whoever wishes to be great among you shall be your *diakonos*, and whoever wishes to be first among you shall be *doulos* of all. For the Son of Man did not come to be ministered to [the verbal form of *diakonos*] but to minister and to give his life a ransom for many.'

But in a massive review of the uses of *diakonia* in the ancient world, J. N. Collins (*Diakonia: Reinterpreting the Ancient Sources*, Oxford University Press, 1990) has argued that the root meaning of this word is 'mediation': it is the action of those 'who operate in an in-between capacity, especially people (or spirits) who implement the desires or intentions of another'. Thus Hermes, the messenger of the gods, is called the *diakonos* of the gods because he mediates their will and their word to others'. A deacon at table is not simply 'waiting in service upon others', but is 'mediating' between the kitchen and the table, sometimes, for example, by tasting the food to test for poison (p. 155). It is the activity which is important, not the servility.

As the organized ministry of the Church developed, deacons might be understood as mediating between a distant overseer (or bishop) and a local community, not simply serving, but also bearing authority — just as Jesus himself 'diaconised', because he mediated the authority of God through his own person. There is nothing here that a woman cannot do; and women are, indeed, described as deacons in the early Church, mediating authority even over men.

Thus, the meaning of words is never fixed or known simply by looking them up in a dictionary. It follows that there is no single 'meaning' of these texts about women (as any commentary will show), and these texts have, indeed, been open to many different interpretations. There is no straightforward meaning of a text on which all agree and from which it can be concluded that the ordination of women is prohibited. In the words of *Porgy and Bess*:

> Them things that you're liable
> To read in the Bible,
> They ain't necessarily so.

However, once again, let us suppose that we could all come to an agreement on the meaning of particular words in the Bible, even then we cannot know 'what the Bible means';

and this brings us to the third of the three reasons why agreed and determinative meanings of Scripture cannot be found. The meaning of any passage carries with it both of the two earlier insecurities, but then amplifies them, because the meaning of any passage is almost limitless. Who decides (and on what grounds) which of many possible meanings is the correct one? An authoritarian system will propose a decision-making process to answer that question, but this is an observation about systems, not about truth.

Hermeneutics

This brings us to the heart of hermeneutics. Here Hermes, the Greek god, flies in on his winged sandals once more. The word 'hermeneutics' is derived from the name Hermes, and it refers, roughly, to these issues of how a message is conveyed through a text to a reader.

At the heart of hermeneutics is the question, 'Whose meaning is the meaning of the meaning?' When we ask the question, 'What does this passage in the New Testament mean?', then we have to ask, 'Whose meaning are we looking for?' Are we looking for the meaning the original author intended to convey, or that of the Church community that associated it with other documents into what became the canonical New Testament, or of the Biblical commentary, or of the preacher, or of the individual who reads the text, or, in a theological perspective, of God?

In a comparable way, when we ask for the meaning of a play such as *The Merchant of Venice*, are we asking what Shakespeare meant when he wrote the text, or what critics of the play through the ages have made of the text, or what a producer of the play at the National Theatre sees in the text, or what you as an individual find in the text when you see or read the play, or some combination of them all?

What we have to realize in reading a text, whether of Scripture or of Shakespeare (or of any other kind), is that the text offers not one single 'meaning', but, rather, the opportunities of meaning and interpretation. John Barton once produced *The Merchant of Venice* with two different actors, Patrick Stewart and David Suchet, playing the part of Shylock in close succession. John Barton said of this experience:

> Basically I gave Patrick and David the same directions and made the same points, both in detail and in general, yet the result was utterly different and individual.
>
> J. L. Halio, *Understanding Shakespeare's Plays in Performance*, Manchester University Press, 1988, pp. 35f.

How could this come about? Obviously because the two actors 'read' the play and the character differently, and the difference created a different style in consequence. In Jay Halio's summary:

> Consider the question of Shylock's Jewishness. How 'Jewish' is he, that is, how much should the fact of his Jewishness be emphasized in performance? Patrick Stewart argues that Shylock's Jewishness is irrelevant, a distraction when emphasized; he is essentially an alien, an outsider who happens to be a Jew . . . . David Suchet cannot agree. For him, Shylock is an outsider because he is a Jew . . . . Although both actors concur that the play is not anti-Semitic (despite the anti-Semitism it contains), they recognize that in the latter part of the twentieth century this aspect cannot be ignored; it must be reckoned with. That each of them did so in quite different ways leading to quite different performances indicates the richness of the character and the possibilities for interpretation.
>
> p. 36.

'Opportunities of meaning', 'possibilities for interpretation' — these are the all-important phrases. And we can see this creative attention to text and meaning already in operation in the early Church. The text of what was to them Scripture (the final boundaries of the Jewish Canon had yet to be fixed) was an opportunity for the Holy Spirit, not a dictation of a single meaning or interpretation of what they should do or believe. The Christian use of what they were later to call the Old Testament was, to say the least, creative.

But how could this apparent contradiction come about — that the Bible was for the early Christians the Word of

God, containing both command and instruction, and yet it did not dictate final and conclusive instructions to them, any more than it does to Christians in the present day? When we see the answer to this, then we can see more clearly how it comes about that the New Testament may contain specific instructions to local church communities about the status and behaviour of women, but that these cannot be converted into command and instruction for *all* communities in *all* circumstances; and that to say this does not subvert the claim, within the Christian system, that the New Testament also is the Word of God.

The frame problem

The relation of text to decision making can most easily be understood in the context of what is known as the frame problem in work on Artificial Intelligence (see earlier, p. 54). We all know how fast computers work, and how difficult it is to beat a computer at chess, yet, in fact, the largest and fastest computer will never arrive at the best solution to a problem unless the programmer gives it a frame in which to operate. A computer *is* extremely good at arriving at the best solution in a game of chess, but only because it has been given the frame or boundary of rules and moves by the programmer (even then, it is hard for the computer programme to resist a fairly immediate gain at the expense of a very much later position; thus, most programmes do not decline the Queen's pawn gambit). So, unless the programmer has, in a sense, provided the possible solutions to a problem, the computer will search for ever. If I raise my hand, will someone die in China? Maybe, but the human brain brackets out a remote consideration of this kind because, otherwise, life would obviously be unliveable. A computer may be fast, but it cannot do what the human brain does characteristically, unless the programmer gives it what are known as 'context-dependent instructions'.

Some religions seem, at first sight, to be operating in exactly the same way: instead of setting people free in a vast ocean of equal opportunities, they give context-dependent rules to set a frame for human action: 'You shall keep the sabbath day holy', and so on. These are the religions of instruction — of Torah in the case of the Jews, of Qur'an in the case of Islam. However, as the Jews very rapidly found out, even context-dependent instructions need much further definition. What does it *mean* to keep the sabbath day holy, in detail and in practice? In March 1986, Rabbi Moshe Feinstein died in New York. He was regarded as the world's leading *posek* (one who knows how to apply law to life). It used to be said that a newly qualified rabbi needed only two things — his ordination certificate and Rabbi Feinstein's telephone number. Thus, 'Can a Jew go up in a lift on the Sabbath?' Answer, 'Yes, provided it is programmed to stop at every floor without pressing a button'. So, even with context-dependent rules, there is still an endless task of applying them in practice. There is a Jewish saying that the mass of rules about the Sabbath in the Mishnah are 'a mountain hanging by a hair'.

It was into a context-control religion that Jesus was born, but, far from spending his time elaborating the detail of context-dependent rules, he moved in exactly the opposite direction. What he offered instead was deliberately context-*in*dependent command. What, he was asked, is the *kelal*, the summary of the law? The love of God and the love of one's neighbour as oneself. And what help is that? The frame problem, far from being solved, is immediately created, because we are left without specific application in a vast ocean of possibility. This is why we find Paul and other New Testament writers trying to solve the frame problem by making the context-independent command into context-dependent instruction: what does love, *agape*, mean, between husbands and wives, parents and children, owners and slaves? How should people behave when they gather together for worship? And, as Paul tries to do this, as he writes to the Christians at Corinth, even he throws up his pen in despair (or breaks off his dictation) and reverts to the context-independent command: 'Look', he says, 'Let me just tell you the more excellent way in which to decide what to do': 'If I speak with the tongues of men and of angels, but have not *agape*, I am become sounding brass and a tinkling cymbal . . .' — the famous chapter 13 of I Corinthians.

So, what *look* like rules or laws in the New Testament are, in fact, context-dependent applications of the context-independent command of love. What we cannot do is then convert those applications into a new kind of law, as though the applications for those particular contexts become a command for all subsequent contexts, from now until the end of time. They may become what are known as 'middle-term axioms', applications and advice that are so normative (cf. p. 115) that it is hard to imagine any circumstance in which they would not be the right basis of action. However, they do not function as law, and there may, therefore, be other applications which, far from resembling middle-term axioms, belong only to local advice. Paul was clearly aware of the distinction, though he could not, obviously, express it in these terms. 'All things are lawful', he wrote, 'But not all things are expedient, not all things are edifying. What controls the judgement is not conformity, but consideration of one's neighbour — "let each of us seek her neighbour's good"' (I Cor. 10. 23ff.).

Does all this mean that the Bible can be ignored by Christians altogether (in a Situation Ethics of 'love and do what you will')? Clearly not, because, in a Christian perspective, the New Testament is itself a consequence of the initiative of God, in which the frame of human decision making is established. The Bible quite clearly delimits the boundaries of appropriate behaviour, but not, for Christians, by way of law. From the context of the command of love, and from the recognition of the first ways in which this context-independent command was made context-dependent for the circumstances of an earlier time, Christians, in turn, are constrained into the applications of love in the contexts in which they now live.

It is in this way that the continuing process of body-culture coevolution is related to the religious points of legitimizing reference. In all religions, there are points of reference in the past, which may or may not be described in terms of revelation, but which, in any case, constrain this process from the past. The ways in which this constraint is brought to bear range from the direct to the indirect; the imitation of Muhammad is not the same as the imitation of Christ. The more direct the constraint is allowed (or required) to be, the more the ideal will be the reproduction of some perfect, or more perfect, 'age of faith' — the period of the ar-Rashidun in Islam, or, for a few who misunderstand the nature of God's action in Christ, of the New Testament in Christianity. If the constraint is indirect, it remains none the less constraint (that condition of greater freedom, p. 169). In that case, it is simply that the procedures of application involve a dialectic between past and present, not a direct reflection of the past into the present.

The difference can be seen in the slogan that was devised some years ago to boost the sale of eggs: 'Go to work on an egg'. This is a context-independent command. You could not literally *do* what it commands. The advertisements, though, used to portray an office worker being transported to work on a mobile egg, and that makes the point. So, how do you make the context-independent command context-dependent? You fry, scramble, poach, boil eggs; you maybe write a recipe book which tells others how to make an *oeuf en cocotte*. But although someone, somewhere, must take an egg and eat it in order to make the context-independent command into a context-dependent application, there are many different ways of turning the command into event. There is, indeed, a limit on the ways in which an egg can be consumed, but there is not just one single way in which to go to work on an egg.

Where Christians are concerned, the command of Jesus is to go to the world in love. The New Testament gives some immediate applications. They become a part of the advice that Christians subsequently appropriate in order to do what Christ requires, but they are not a substitute for the command, particularly where they seem to conflict with the command — exactly as Wesley (and others) perceived in the case of slavery. They are the recipe of our redemption, but they are not rules that supply the only way in which an egg can be cooked or in which our neighbour can be loved. For, here, the metaphor breaks down, because what Christ promised was *not* a recipe book of invariable rules, but the reign of God and the gift of the Holy Spirit. It was the experience of the Holy Spirit in life, in the actual boiling and breaking of the eggs, that the applications were made in the New Testament. They now set the frame for our own solutions, but do not dictate a single recipe as the only regulation for all time.

What, in practice, did this mean in the New Testament period? Let us, for a moment, stop boiling eggs and consider the most divisive issue in the early Church, the status of gentiles who joined the new covenant.

Jews existed, in their own perception, because of God's command to their ancestors: 'Be holy, as I am holy' — another context-independent command. What it meant to be holy was then made more context-dependent in Torah as a whole, although, as we have seen, not exhaustively so. Jews were to keep the laws and live in the covenant, not for their own sake, but for the sake of the whole world, 'until the knowledge of God shall cover the earth as the waters cover the sea' (Habakkuk 2.14; contrast Isaiah 11.9, where the vision is more restricted). So Judaism, at the time when Jesus was alive, was a strongly missionary religion, and many gentiles were associated with the covenant, either as God-fearers or by being brought formally inside the boundary of the covenant, in which case they took upon themselves the keeping of the terms of the covenant in the specific laws, and, if they were men, they were circumcised.

Jesus broke open the boundaries of the covenant by insisting that the true condition of being related to God is not defined by the covenant-boundary, but by the faith that God is, and that God can make every difference to life in the direction of healing and love. Through his resurrection and ascension, the experience of the power of God (the *dunamis* of God in the Greek) made the *new* covenant an exodus (Luke 9.31) from death into life.

But what of gentiles who wanted to become part of this new understanding of the covenant with God? Did they have to keep all the terms and conditions of the law? Should they, for example, be circumcised? It was an issue as divisive in the Church of that day as the ordination of women has proved to be in our own, because it clearly raised the question of the very essence of the redeemed, God-bearing community. Acts chapter 15 records the controversy in something like a meeting of a general synod, and James concluded the long discussion (in Greek, *zetesis*, seeking or searching) by giving his verdict that gentiles need only keep some minimal boundary conditions, not the whole of Torah. His decision is based on the foundation of Scripture: 'This is entirely in harmony with the words of the prophets', quoting Amos 9.11 and 12 — using the Greek word *sumphoneo*, which we recognize in the word 'symphony'. There is nothing here of a dictation; it is, rather, a visionary application. James also pointed out that, in any case, there are those who will be maintaining the foundation of Torah every week in the synagogues and in their lives: 'For Moses has always had his preachers in every town and is read aloud in the synagogues every sabbath'.

Having reached this decision, how did they communicate it to Antioch? 'It has seemed good to us and to the Holy Spirit . . .'. Not, 'It has been found in Scripture', but, rather, that on the foundation of the promises and purposes of God which can be discerned in Scripture, they are making this attempt to achieve and realize them now.

This was a change at least as momentous as the extension of the priesthood of all believers to the particular ministries of bishops, priests, and deacons, and now to the extension of these ministries to women, and, in fact, the two styles of being Christian — observing Torah or not observing Torah — coexisted for another three or four centuries. It still remains a minority account of the recognition of Jesus as Christ that it requires an acceptance of the law. What proves good to the Holy Spirit is not always or immediately exclusive. However, at the same time, what does seem good to the Holy Spirit, after long *zetesis* on the basis of experience, cannot be postponed for ever. Christians are necessarily committed to the translation of these context-independent foundations of command into the context-dependent circumstances of their time.

So, Paul and others brought this new evocation and command of love, of *agape*, to bear on their own world and circumstances. It began to change that world in the direction of love, but it did not change the world as though it were the easy composition of an inferior fiction — 'with one mighty leap, Jack was free': slaves were *not* free for almost another two thousand years. Neither Paul, nor, for that matter, Aristotle, could think how, in practice, a world without slavery (or without patriarchy) could be run. Yet already, Paul insisted, patriarchy and slavery must be constrained, and thus tempered, by love. And, because he was himself constrained by love, he was moved by the Holy Spirit in the context of his existing world to begin the long process by which there is an increasing realization in the present of what will in the end be the case, when there is neither Jew nor Greek, slave nor free, male and female.

It is this process which brings religion (in this case Christianity) into an effective relation with body-culture coevolution because it becomes a constraint over its direction. For, this commitment (in the Christian case) to the composition of the world by the hard work of love cannot end at the boundary of the New Testament canon. The women and men of that time began the process in relation to the circumstances in which they lived. It is for Christians after them to look to the New Testament for the direction in which they set out — the frame of the impetus of love — and to carry it much further, assisted, as they were, by the constant self-donation of God to those who do not refuse the leading of the Holy Spirit. And, just as the Bible reveals a constant contradiction of itself — of earlier beliefs and values by later ones — as the people of God learned more deeply the nature of the One with whom they have to deal, so later Christians have sometimes to transcend, even perhaps to contradict, some of the ways in which the first followers of Jesus put into practice, by way of context-dependent applications, their experience of being the resurrection community of Christ. Christians, too, can 'see further than their ancestors because they stand on the shoulders of giants'; 'There are many things I have to show you, but you cannot bear them yet' (John 16.12).

The authority of Scripture

None of this affects the authority of Scripture, but here, too, we have to recognize *change*. For almost two thousand years, many Christians thought that the books of Scripture had been directly dictated by the Holy Spirit, and that the Biblical writers simply took the words down as inerrant recorders. As recently as 1920, the encyclical *Spiritus Paraclitus*, cast a bridge back across the centuries to Jerome (who died in 420), when it wrote of him establishing the Catholic doctrine,

> that the sacred books are written under the inspiration of the Holy Spirit, have God for their author, and were as such entrusted to the Church. Indeed he asserts that the books of Holy Scripture were written under the inspiration of the Holy Spirit, by His instruction, stimulus and even dictation, and were indeed written and produced by Him.

That the books that are recognized and accepted as Scripture would not have come into existence without God is not at issue within the boundary of the Christian Church. What have been abandoned are the words, 'and even dictation'; or, to put it in more general terms, what has been abandoned is a dictation theory of how these books came into being as a consequence of God's initiative. What these books reveal is a long process of God's willingness to redeem and repair the brokenness of the human condition, to establish a new covenant in a reconciliation which for Christians is made real repeatedly in that great reunion party that is called the Eucharist. Scripture is the consequence of this patient process, of which it is itself the record, through which God evokes recognition and reply without coercing or bypassing the idiosyncratic circumstance of the people with whom he has to deal.

Thus the Bible contains constant correction of itself as the relationship with God was found to be trustworthy, even through catastrophe, suffering and sin. Traditions accumulate and eventually converge, through which a succession of generations came to know more wisely, more penitently and more hopefully, the One with whom they have to deal.

However, at no point did God dictate words which would override the enculturated character of a person in her or his historical and social and geographical context. That view (as Athenagoras summarized it in the second century), according to which the Biblical writers were as passive as a flute when it is played by a flautist, has gone. Even Dr Packer, who signed the *Church Times* letter (p. 245) opposing the ordination of women to the presbyterate, argued this very point in one of his earliest books, *Fundamentalism and the Word of God* (London, IVF, 1958):

> Because Evangelicals hold that the biblical writers were completely controlled by the Holy Spirit, it is often supposed . . . that they maintain what is called the 'dictation' or 'typewriter' theory of inspiration — namely, that the mental activity of the writers was simply suspended, apart from what was necessary for the mechanical transcription of words supernaturally introduced into their consciousness. But it is not so. This 'dictation theory' is a man of straw. It is safe to say that no Protestant theologian, from the Reformation till now, has ever held it . . . . The proof of this lies in the fact that, when these theologians addressed themselves to the question, What was the Spirit's mode of operating in the writers' minds?, they all gave their answer in terms not of dictation, but of *accommodation*, and rightly maintained that God completely adapted His inspiring activity to the cast of mind, outlook, temperament, interests, literary habits and stylistic idiosyncracies of each writer.

How, then, might the relation between the initiative of God and the consequence of Scripture be better understood? Packer advocated the use of the word 'concursive':

> We are to think of the Spirit's inspiring activity, and, for that matter, of all His regular operations in and upon human personality, as (to use an old but valuable technical

term) *concursive*; that is, as exercised in, through and by means of the writer's own activity, in such a way that their thinking and writing was *both* free and spontaneous on their part *and* divinely elicited and controlled, and what they wrote was not only their own work but also God's work
p. 80.

That word and that understanding are now very widely accepted in all parts of the Church. However, because this is so, it makes the added clause in the *Church Times'* letter disingenuous in the extreme — 'cultural conditioning notwithstanding'. Cultural conditioning is *never* 'notwithstanding', it is the medium through which God chose to reveal his purpose and practice of redemption. No doubt, if God had wished to do so, he could have sent words into the world unaffected by the personality of the prophet through whom they are sent. This is exactly what Muslims claim to be the case with the Qur'an. The content of the Qur'an is laid up with God in heaven, and he sends the same essential message through every prophet, culminating in Muhammad. So if you wish to know what is possible and impossible for women (what is *halal wa'l-haram*, allowed and forbidden), the Qur'an will tell you, cultural conditioning notwithstanding.

But the Bible is not Qur'an, as Muslims will be the first to point out. The Bible does *not* dictate behaviours to Christians as the Qur'an dictates behaviours to Muslims. Christians believe that God sent into the world, not inerrant words but the unerring Word, who was without sin; that God gave, not inerrant words but his only Son, to the end that all that believe in him should not perish, but have everlasting life.

It is the patience of God, in the Christian perspective, and the faith of those who built up the gradual recognition of his nature in his quest, which made the Incarnation possible. To that human life and being of Jesus, God was constantly present as constraint, so that he was and is truly both God and man without confusion of the two. But that certainly did not produce the life of a dictator. Jesus,

in the same pattern, did not coerce, but, rather, evoked new
directions and new consequences ('repent', 'be healed') in
the lives of those whom he met — and, now, in many lives
beyond those first encounters. Beyond his death and resurrection, the same Holy Spirit who was present to the sustaining of his life is present to the transformation of other
lives in the direction of love, joy, peace, patience, kindness,
goodness, trustfulness, gentleness, and self-control — those
gifts of the Spirit (Galatians 5.19) that have nothing to do
with the dictation of our behaviours. Indeed, Paul immediately added the comment in Galatians, 'No law can touch
such things as these'.

If, then, the Bible is not the Qur'an, to use it as though it
is the Qur'an is a denial of the Incarnation and a refusal of
the gift of the Holy Spirit. But in that case, in what way
does the Bible have authority in relation to ourselves? The
answer lies in the close relation of the two words 'author'
and 'authority'. These, in turn, reflect the close connection
between the two Latin words *auctor* and *auctoritas*. In the
Latin dictionary of Lewis and Short, *auctor* is defined as
'he that brings about the existence of any object, or promotes the increase or prosperity of it, whether he first
originates it, or by his efforts gives greater permanence or
continuance to it'. It is an excellent definition of the Biblical
understanding of creation. From it flows the meaning of
auctoritas. Basically, it has to do with an *auctor*, an author,
bringing something into being, an invention. So, it also
means an opinion, or advice, or encouragement. It means
weight, or importance, hence power and our sense of
authority; to have the power to bring something into being
involves the right, and also the responsibility, to bring
something into being, the authority to do so.

God is the *auctor*, the author of all things. He is the
unproduced Producer of all that is who continues to sustain
every moment and every aspect of his creation in being.
Without him, we would not be. In his quest for our redemption, not by coercion, but by the cooperations of faith, he
brought into being the words that now stand as Scripture.
He is the source of these words because he is the source of

the lives that wrote them, evoking this particular consequence, and, in this sense, he is their author; and because
he is their author, they have authority: they are the means
through which his authorship continues now in human
lives, so that a new and different story can be told through
them, a story of love, joy, peace, thanksgiving, and those
many other gifts of the Spirit. 'With one mighty leap, Jack
is free'; but the Holy Spirit still has to work on the given-
ness of our idiosyncratic character, experience and history
to transform us in the direction of love. Our attention to
the words of Scripture is a first and foundational means
through which this authority, this work of authorship, is
exercised in our case. However, if a dictation theory of the
relation of God to Scripture has been abandoned (as it necessarily has), it would be bizarre to maintain a dictation
theory of the relation of Scripture to life.

So, what this means in practice is that if we wish to find
'the meaning of the Bible' for us, it is always, to use a
familiar phrase, a fusion of two horizons. We go back to the
original text, trying to understand it as best we may in the
original horizon of its time and context, knowing that such
exegesis is always provisional and incomplete because we
cannot know the final and absolute meaning of any text at
all. We encounter God in the *opportunities* of interpretation
in the text, allowing him to unfold the meanings of his
mercy and the ever-changing demands of his love. We do
this by connecting this original horizon with our own — the
time and the context in which we live now. This fusion of
these two horizons then creates a new and God-endowed
perspective on the world in which we live.

In this perspective, it becomes obvious that there is no
warrant in Scripture for refusing the ordination of women
to the presbyterate or priesthood. The texts which speak of
male headship and authority could not speak of anything
else in the world of that time, because culture is never
'notwithstanding'.

Yet, already those texts are speaking of headship tempered by love. So, now and at last, it can be seen beyond
doubt that, just as the true 'tempering by love' of slavery

was its abolition, so the true 'tempering by love' of patriarchy is its abolition.

Thus, the texts quoted earlier (pp. 245–6) are better
understood as boundary markers on the road to freedom,
not least because they are controlled by Paul's vision (p.
241) of the consequence of Christ: 'For as many of you as
have been baptized have been clothed in Christ. There is
neither Jew nor Greek, there is neither slave nor free,
there is not male and female'. The meaning of this passage,
in detail, is bound to be as uncertain as any other, but, in
general, it points to a condition where the classic divisions
of that time have been obliterated by the love which led
Christ to a cross. If *this* is the consequence of baptism, then
not only must the traditional attitudes of a patriarchal
society be abolished, but the Church should be far out in
front, urging the world to its wisdom by the example which
it lives. For 'Christ is risen from the dead'. This is not some
formula merely to be recited each year on Easter Day. It is
the singular truth which will kick-start the economy of a
life into love if, indeed, it is believed, and, if, indeed, Christ
has been put on as a garment. Touching the hem of that
garment, which was stripped from him before he was led
out to die, it would be a terrifying betrayal to turn to the
daughters of Eve and of Mary and say that they cannot
handle the body and blood of Christ. In the words of a
searching poem by Frances Frank,

> Did the woman say
> When she held him for the last time
> > In the dark rain on the hill-top
> > After the pain, and bleeding, and the dying,
> 'This is my body, this is my blood'?

If then, why not now?

Bibliography

Alexander, R. D., *Darwinism and Human Affairs*. University of Washington Press 1979.

Alexander, R. M., review of T. A. McMahon and J. T. Bonner, 'On Size and Life' (*Times Higher Educational Supplement*, 1984).

al-Qaradawi, Y., *The Lawful and Prohibited in Islam*. American Trust Publications, n.d.

Aquinas, T., *Summa contra Gentiles*.

Ashby, W. R., *An Introduction to Cybernetics*. Chapman and Hall 1964.

Auerbach, E., *Mimesis: dargestellte Wirklichkeit in der abendländischen Literatur*. Franke 1946.

Ball, J. A., 'Memes as Replicators' (*Ethology and Sociobiology*, V, 1984).

Banton, M., ed., *Darwinism and the Study of Society*. University of Chicago Press 1961.

Barash, D. P., *Sociobiology and Behavior*. Elsevier 1977.

— *The Whisperings Within: Evolution and the Origin of Human Nature*. Harper and Row 1979.

Behr-Siegel, E., *The Ministry of Women in the Church*. Oakwood Publications 1991.

Berlin, B. and Kay, P., *Basic Colour Terms: Their Universality and Evolution*. University of California Press 1969.

Borek, E., *The Atoms Within Us*. Columbia University Press 1980.

Bowker, J. W., *The Sense of God: Sociological, Anthropological and Psychological Approaches to the Origin of the Sense of God*. Oxford University Press 1973; new edn, One World Press 1995.

— *The Religious Imagination and the Sense of God*. Oxford University Press 1978.

— 'On Being Religiously Human' (*Zygon*, XVI, 1981), pp. 365–82.

265

— ed., 'Origins, Functions and Management of Aggression in Biocultural Evolution' (*Zygon*, XVIII, 1983).
— *Worlds of Faith: Religious Belief and Practice in Britain Today*. Ariel Books 1983.
— *Licensed Insanities*. Darton, Longman and Todd 1987 (U.S. edn, *Is Anybody Out There?*. Christian Classics 1988).
— 'Cosmology, Religion and Society' (*Zygon*, XXV, 1990).
— *The Meanings of Death*. Cambridge University Press 1991.
— 'Christianity and Non-Christian Religions: A Neo-Darwinian Revolution?' in ed., A. Sharma, *God, Truth and Reality*. Macmillan 1993.
Brandon, R. N. and Burian, R. M., *Genes, Organisms, Populations: Controversies Over the Units of Selection*. MIT Press 1987.
Burnett, M., *The Endurance of Life: The Implications of Genetics for Human Life*. Cambridge University Press 1978.
Bynum, C. W., *Jesus as Mother: Studies in the Spirituality of the High Middle Ages*. University of California Press 1982.
— *Holy Feast and Holy Fast*. University of California Press 1987.
Calow, P., *Biological Machines: A Cybernetic Approach to Life*. Arnold 1976.
Cavalli-Sforza, L. L. and Feldman, M. W., *Cultural Transmission and Evolution*. Princeton University Press 1981.
Collins, J. N., *Diakonia: Reinterpreting the Ancient Sources*. Oxford University Press 1990.
Crick, F., *What Mad Pursuit: A Personal View of Scientific Discovery*. Weidenfeld 1988.
Curnock, N., ed., *The Journals of the Rev. John Wesley, A.M.* London 1909–16.
d'Aquili, E. G., *Biogenetic Structuralism*. Columbia University Press 1974.
— ed., *The Spectrum of Ritual*. Columbia University Press 1979.
— with C. D. Laughlin and J. McManus, *Brain, Symbol and Experience: Toward a Neurophenomenology of Human Consciousness*. New Science Library 1990.
Dawkins, R., *The Selfish Gene*. Oxford University Press 1976, 1989.
— *The Extended Phenotype*. W. H. Freeman 1982.
— *Viruses of the Mind*. British Humanist Association 1992.
Digby, A., 'Women's Biological Straitjacket' in S. Mendus and J. Rendall, eds., *Sexuality and Subordination*. Routledge 1989.
Doi, A. R., *Shariah: The Islamic Law*. Ta Ha Publishers 1984.
Doolittle, W. F. and Sapienza, C., 'Selfish Genes, the Phenotype Paradigm and Genome Evolution' (*Nature*, 284, 1980), pp. 601–7.

Dostoevsky, F. M., *The Brothers Karamazov*. 1878–80.

Duckworth, D., *Views on Some Social Subjects*. 1915.

Durham, W. H., *Coevolution: Genes, Culture and Human Diversity*. Stanford University Press 1991.

Eigen, M. and Schuster, P., *The Hypercycle: A Principle of Natural Self-Organisation*. Springer-Verlag 1979.

Ekman, P., *The Face of Man: Expressions of Universal Emotions in a New Guinea Village*. Garland 1980.

Epp, E. J., *The Theological Tendency of Codex Bezae Cantabrigensis in Acts*. Cambridge University Press 1966.

Erikson, K., *Wayward Puritans: A Study in the Sociology of Deviance*. Macmillan 1986.

Evrie, J. van, *Negroes and Negro Slavery: The First an Inferior Race – the Latter its Normal Condition*. Baltimore 1853.

S. Faludi, *Backlash: The Undeclared War Against Women*. Chatto and Windus 1992.

Fitzmyer, J. A., *Romans: A New Translation with Introduction and Commentary*. Geoffrey Chapman 1993.

Flaubert, G., *Trois Contes* (1877) in *Oeuvres Completes*. Seuil, l'Integrale 1964.

Flinn, M. V. and Alexander, R. D., 'Culture Theory: The Developing Synthesis from Biology' (*Human Ecology*, X, 1982).

Gershon, E. S. *et al.*, 'Transmitted Factors in the Morbid Risk of Affective Disorders: A Controlled Study' (*Journal of Psychiatric Research*, XII, 1975), pp. 283–99.

Gleick, J., *Genius: Richard Feynmann and Modern Physics*. Little, Brown 1992.

Graves, C. L., *Mr Punch's History of Modern England*. Cassell 1921.

Halio, J. L., *Understanding Shakespeare's Plays in Performance*. Manchester University Press 1988.

Haribhadra, *Yogadristisamuccaya*.

Harvey, P., *An Introduction to Buddhism*. Cambridge University Press 1990.

Honore, D. D., *Trevor Huddleston: Essays on his Life and Work*. Oxford University Press 1988.

Jinasena, *Adipurana*.

Johnson, M. H. and Morton, J., *Biology and Cognitive Development: The Case of Face Recognition*. Blackwell 1991.

Johnson, P., *Equal in Monastic Profession*. University of Chicago Press 1994.

Kramisch, S., *Exploring India's Sacred Art*. University of Pennsylvania Press 1983.

Lefebvre, M., *An Open Letter to Confused Catholics*. Fowler Wright Books 1986.

Long, M., *Right to Choose?* Christian Focus Publications 1993.

Lumsden, C. J. and Wilson, E. O., *Genes, Mind and Culture*. Harvard University Press 1981.

— *Promethean Fire: Reflections on the Origin of Mind*. Harvard University Press 1983.

Mahoney, J., *The Making of Moral Theology*. Clarendon Press 1987.

Marantz, P. and Stein, J. G., *Peace-Making in the Middle East: Problems and Prospects*. Croom Helm 1985.

Marty, M. E. and Appleby, R. S., eds., *Fundamentalisms Observed*. Chicago University Press 1991.

Maudsley, H., 'Sex in Mind and Education' (*Fortnightly Review*, XXI, 1874).

Maycock, A. L., *The Inquisition from its Establishment to the Great Schism*. Constable 1926.

Mayo, O., *Natural Selection and its Constraints*. Academic Press 1983.

McGinley, P., *Times Three*. New York 1960.

— *Saint-Watching*. Thomas More 1982.

McLaughlin, E., 'Christ My Mother: Feminine Naming and Metaphor in Medieval Spirituality' (*Nasotah Review*, XV, 1975), pp. 228–48.

Mecklin, J., *The Passing of a Saint: A Study in Culture Types*. University of Chicago Press 1941.

Mendus, S. and Rendall, J., eds., *Sexuality and Subordination*. Routledge 1989.

Ohno, S., 'The Development of Sexual Reproduction' in C. R. Austin and R. V. Short, *The Evolution of Reproduction*. Cambridge University Press 1976.

Oyama, S., *The Ontogeny of Information*. Cambridge University Press 1985.

Packer, J., *Fundamentalism and the Word of God*. IVF 1958.

Paige, K. E. and J. M., *The Politics of Reproductive Ritual*. University of California Press 1981.

Pattee, H. H., 'Laws and Constraints, Symbols and Language' in ed. C. H. Waddington, *Towards a Theoretical Biology*. Edinburgh University Press 1972.

Pugh, G. E., *The Biological Origin of Human Values*. Basic Books 1977.

Pulliam, H. R. and Dunford, C., *Programmed to Learn: An Essay on the Evolution of Culture*. Columbia University Press 1980.

Rappoport, A. R., *Pigs for Ancestors*. Yale University Press 1968.

Ray, V. F., 'Human Color Perception and Behavioural Response' (*Transactions of the New York Academy of Science*, XVI, 1953).

Ruyle, E. E. *et al.*, 'The Adaptive Significance of Cultural Behaviour' (*Human Ecology*, V, 1977).

Ryle, G., *Dilemmas*. Cambridge University Press 1954.

Schulenberg, J., 'Sexism and the Celestial Gynaeceum' (*Journal of Medieval History*, IV, 1978), pp. 117–33.

— 'Female Sanctity: Public and Private Roles, ca. 500–1100' in M. Erler and M. Kowaleski, eds., *Women and Power in the Middle Ages*. University of Georgia Press 1988.

Sharma, A., *God, Truth and Reality*. Macmillan 1993.

Shweder, R. A. and Bourne, E. J., 'Does the Concept of a Person Vary Cross-culturally?' in ed. R. A. Shweder and R. A. LeVine, *Culture Theory: Essays on Mind Self, and Emotion*. Cambridge University Press 1984.

Smith, W. J., *The Behaviour of Communicating: An Ethological Approach*. Harvard University Press 1980.

Thompson, W., *Appeal of One Half of the Human Race, Women, Against the Pretensions of the Other Half, Men, to Retain Them in Political, and Thence in Civil and Domestic Slavery*. 1825.

Thoreau, H., *Walden*. 1854.

Tibble, A., *John Clare: The Journals, Essays, and The Journey from Essex*. Manchester, Carcanet New Press, 1980.

Trivers, R. L., 'The Evolution of Reciprocal Altruism' (*Quarterly Review of Biology*, XLVI, 1976).

Weinstein, D. and Bell, R. M., *Saints and Society: The Two Worlds of Western Christendom, 1000–1700*. University of Chicago Press 1982.

Wesley, J., *An Earnest Appeal to Men of Reason and Religion*. Dublin 1806.

Williams, G. C., *Adaptation and Natural Selection*. Princeton 1966.

Wilson, E. O. (see also C. J. Lumsden), *Sociobiology: The New Synthesis*. Harvard University Press 1975.

— *On Human Nature*. Harvard University Press 1978.

Wish, H., ed., *Ante-Bellum: The Writings of George Fitzhugh and Hinton Rowan Helper on Slavery*. Putnam 1960.

Wyschogrod, E., *Saints and Post-Modernism: Revisioning Moral Philosophy*. University of Chicago Press 1990.

Index